A LECTIONARY PSALTER

Psalms and Gospel Acclamations for Sundays, Solemnities and Feasts for the Three-year Lectionary Cycle

BY JOHN SCHIAVONE

A Lectionary Psalter
Psalms and Gospel Acclamations for Sundays, Solemnities and Feasts
  for the Three-year Lectionary Cycle
by John Schiavone

© 2003, OCP Publications
5536 NE Hassalo, Portland, OR 97213
(503) 281-1191
liturgy@ocp.org   www.ocp.org   www.liturgy.com

Published with the approval of the Committee on the Liturgy, United States Conference of Catholic Bishops.

CREDITS

John J. Limb, *Publisher;* Paulette McCoy, *Editorial Director*

Randall DeBruyn, *Executive Editor*

Steve Grundy, *Project Editor;* Barbara Bridge, Glenn CJ Byer, Bernice (Bunny) Hatch, C. Angelyn Jáuregui, Melinda Atkins Loomis, Anne Mucken, Gus Pappelis, Marie Phillippi, Michael R. Prendergast, Pam Ruckhaber, Lori Rux, Eric Schumock, Amanda Weller, Nancy Wolf, *Editing Assistance*

Sharon Norton, *Music Engraving Director;* Shannon McNerney, *Music Engraving*

Jean Germano, *Art Director;* Le Vu, *Graphic Assistance*

Cover Art: Jean Germano, inspired by King David initial "D" from the *Gloss on the Psalms,* 12th century, now in the Lincoln Cathedral, England.

TABLE OF CONTENTS

RESPONSORIAL PSALMS

GOSPEL ACCLAMATIONS

ASSEMBLY RESPONSES

INDICES

PREFACE

In composing music for worship, I am always interested in the reactions of those who hear and sing what I have written. In response to a particular piece people have often said something like, "That was very prayerful." In asking what is it about this or that piece that makes someone feel prayerful, I have come to this conclusion: I often write liturgical music not in major or minor keys, but rather in the modes that characterize plainchant, the Dorian, Phrygian, Lydian or Mixolydian mode. These diatonic scales are like major or minor keys, but with some notable exceptions. The half-tone steps are in different places on the modal scales. For example, the Mixolydian mode is like the major scale, but with one important exception: the 7th tone on the scale is lower by a half-step. If a Mixolydian tune is in the key of F, the key signature would have two flats, not one, to account for the lowered 7th tone, which would be E-flat, not E-natural. What makes a Mixolydian melody seem prayerful is that the lowered 7th removes the strong dominant-to-tonic progression, so the cadence is not quite so forceful. Is this what makes a piece of music seem prayerful, that the progressions and resolutions are not driven by the strong dominant to tonic tendency that has characterized so much Western music since the 18th and 19th centuries? Is it the "kinder, gentler" cadence that lets the singer or listener down more easily, with more of a sense of wandering and wondering, that makes one feel prayerful?

In this collection of Sunday responsorial psalms and gospel acclamations, I have made a conscious effort to use the above-mentioned modes. They have served more than a millennium and a half of sung prayer. The modes are part of our musical heritage, and they can continue to help a new generation to sing of their faith and hope, to respond to God's word, and to acclaim the Good News. It is important that instrumentalists and cantors pay close attention to the key signatures and the chord progressions, resisting the temptation to revert to the strong dominant to tonic, letting the modes work their own kind of free expression. Will it be "prayerful"? We can't manufacture prayerfulness, but we can do our best to let our art open the minds and imaginations, hearts and wills of those whom we serve in our liturgical ministry of music.

John Schiavone
Whittier, California
January, 2003

INTRODUCTION

The responsorial psalm, also called the gradual, has great liturgical and pastoral significance because it is an "integral part of the liturgy of the word." (GIRM 36) Accordingly, the faithful must be continuously instructed on the way to perceive the word of God speaking in the psalms and to turn these psalms into the prayer of the Church. This, of course, "will be achieved more readily if a deeper understanding of the psalms, according to the meaning with which they are sung in the sacred Liturgy, is more diligently promoted among the clergy and communicated to all the faithful by means of appropriate catechesis." (Laudis canticum) Lectionary for Mass, *Introduction, #19*

SINGING THE PSALMS AND GOSPEL ACCLAMATIONS

ON THE SINGING OF RESPONSES

The psalm and gospel acclamation responses are intended for melody-only singing. Typically the cantor sings the response and the assembly repeats in "responsorial" fashion. For the gospel acclamations, once the assembly has sung a particular alleluia or Lenten acclamation several Sundays in a row, the cantor may choose not to sing the response alone first, but invite the assembly to join in immediately. Descants have been added to selected celebrations of greater solemnity during the liturgical year.

ON THE SINGING OF VERSES

The first preparation for singing the verses is done without the music—they should be read, understood and allowed to emanate from a place of prayer in the hearts of the singers.

The verse settings are chant tones which by their very nature flow in long, lyrical lines. They may be sung by a cantor or SATB choir. While the tones do not draw attention to themselves, these verses should come across as an important part of the whole, not just as "filler" between each repetition of the response, and should be sung in a way that reflects the character of the individual response.

In cases where the number of phrases in a psalm verse is not consistent throughout the psalm, dashed lines in brackets are shown in place of text. These meaures may be omitted without jeopardizing a coherent harmonic progression.

Singers must proclaim the verses with clarity so that the text is understood and its meaning is clear. A cantor can easily make use of *rubato* to emphasize specific words; a choir, however, will have to spend time on coordination to achieve the same effect.

Psalm verses are designed to be sung by a cantor or vocal ensemble and are not intended for use by the assembly. If it is not practical for the verses to be sung, they may be spoken while the accompaniment is played softly as a background. At the end of each verse, the assembly sings the response.

Gospel verses are sung or spoken in the same manner as the psalm verses. It should be noted, however, that according to the *General Instruction of the Roman Missal* and the *Institutio Generalis Missalis Romani, 2002*, if the Alleluia/Gospel Acclamation or Verse before the Gospel is not sung, it is omitted altogether *(GIRM 39, IGMR 63c)*.

Whoever sings the psalm verses plays a vital role in the assembly's participation at this point in the Liturgy of the Word.

ACCOMPANIMENTS

These musical settings are written to be accompanied by keyboard and/or guitar. While some guitar chords reflect a harmony different from the notated keyboard/choral harmony, the chords and keyboard part are compatible and function well together.

The instrumentalist needs to choose an introduction to set the tempo and tonality of the music. If the assembly is largely unfamiliar with the music, the entire response may be helpful to play as an introduction. For responses with which the assembly is more familiar, the final few notes of the response are often adequate.

LITURGY PREPARATION ASSISTANCE

ASSEMBLY RESPONSES

Melody-only assembly responses are provided beginning on page 262 for use in worship bulletins. For reprint permission contact OCP Reprint Permission at 1-800-LITURGY (548-8749) or online at *www.ocp.org/licensing*.

LITURGY.COM, TODAY'S LITURGY AND LITPLAN

Visit *www.liturgy.com*, our online liturgy preparation service. Simple enough for the inexperienced and comprehensive enough for veteran planners, *Liturgy.com* is the most advanced, user-friendly and affordable online liturgy preparation resource available. *Liturgy.com* will give you what you need—when and where you need it.

Today's Liturgy provides helpful articles on a variety of topics to assist you in your preparation of parish liturgy. The magazine also includes preparation pages for each Sunday and feast day of the year.

LitPlan is a liturgy preparation resource in CD-ROM form. The complete contents of twenty popular liturgical resources are included, supplemented annually with updates featuring the new contents of *Breaking Bread* and *Music Issue*. The indexed *LitPlan* database can easily be customized by adding songs from other sources. This way, information about all the songs your parish uses can be organized in one place. You may contact your OCP Customer Service Representative for more information at 1-800-LITURGY (548-8749).

RESPONSORIAL PSALMS

FIRST SUNDAY OF ADVENT — A

Psalm 122: 1–2, 3–4, 4–5, 6–7, 8–9 [1]

RESPONSE: Cantor/All (♩ = *ca. 80*)

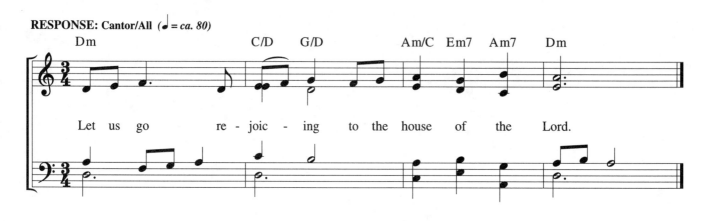

Let us go re-joic-ing to the house of the Lord.

VERSES: Cantor or SATB

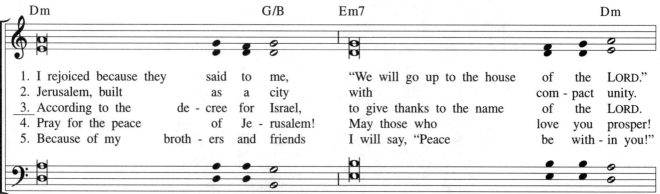

1. I rejoiced because they said to me, "We will go up to the house of the LORD."
2. Jerusalem, built as a city with com-pact unity.
3. According to the de-cree for Israel, to give thanks to the name of the LORD.
4. Pray for the peace of Je-rusalem! May those who love you prosper!
5. Because of my broth-ers and friends I will say, "Peace be with-in you!"

1. And now we have set foot within your gates, O Je-rusalem.
2. To it the tribes go up, the tribes of the LORD.
3. In it are set up judg-ment seats, seats for the house of David.
4. May peace be with-in your walls, prosperity in your buildings.
5. Because of the house of the LORD, our God, I will pray for your good.

Gospel Acclamation for this celebration may be found on page 224.
A separate assembly response may be found on page 267.

First Sunday of Advent — B

Psalm 80: 2–3, 15–16, 18–19 [2]

Gospel Acclamation for this celebration may be found on page 224.
A separate assembly response may be found on page 269.

FIRST SUNDAY OF ADVENT — C

Psalm 25: 4–5, 8–9, 10, 14 [3]

RESPONSE: Cantor/All (♩ = ca. 60)

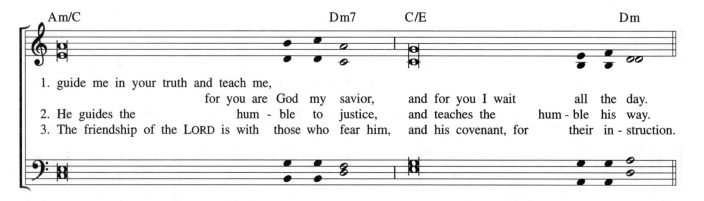

To you, O Lord, I lift___ my soul, I lift___ my soul.___

VERSES: Cantor or SATB

1. Your ways, O LORD, make known to me; teach me your paths,
2. Good and upright is the LORD; thus he shows sin - ners the way.
3. All the paths of the LORD are kind - ness and constancy toward those who keep his covenant and his de - crees.

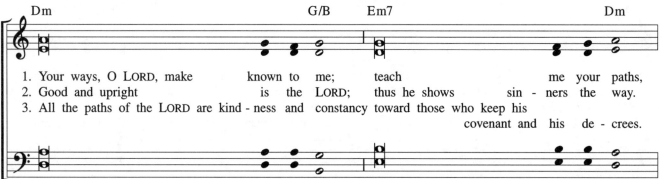

1. guide me in your truth and teach me, for you are God my savior, and for you I wait all the day.
2. He guides the hum - ble to justice, and teaches the hum - ble his way.
3. The friendship of the LORD is with those who fear him, and his covenant, for their in - struction.

Gospel Acclamation for this celebration may be found on page 224.
A separate assembly response may be found on page 276.

SECOND SUNDAY OF ADVENT — A

Psalm 72: 1–2, 7–8, 12–13, 17 [4]

RESPONSE: Cantor/All (♩ = ca. 80)

Jus - tice shall flour-ish in his time,_____ and full - ness of peace for ev - er.___

VERSES: Cantor or SATB

1. O God, with your judgment en - dow the king, and with your justice, the king's son;
2. Justice shall flower in his days, and profound peace, till the moon be no more.
3. For he shall rescue the poor when he cries out, and the afflicted when he has no one to help him.
4. May his name be bless'd for - ever; as long as the sun his name shall re - main.

1. he shall govern your peo - ple with justice and your afflicted ones with judgment.
2. May he rule from sea to sea, and from the River to the ends of the earth.
3. He shall have pity for the lowly and the poor; the lives of the poor he shall save.
4. In him shall all the tribes of the earth be blessed; all the nations shall pro - claim his happiness.

Gospel Acclamation for this celebration may be found on page 224.
A separate assembly response may be found on page 267.

SECOND SUNDAY OF ADVENT — B

Psalm 85: 9–10, 11–12, 13–14 [5]

RESPONSE: Cantor/All (♩ = *ca. 85*)

Lord, let us see your kind-ness, and grant us your sal - va - tion.

VERSES: Cantor or SATB

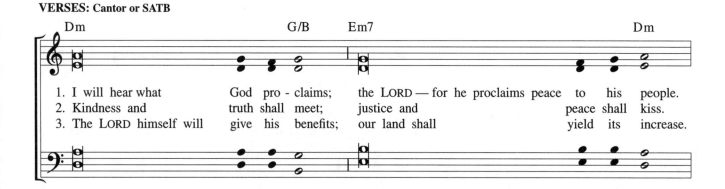

1. I will hear what God pro - claims; the LORD — for he proclaims peace to his people.
2. Kindness and truth shall meet; justice and peace shall kiss.
3. The LORD himself will give his benefits; our land shall yield its increase.

1. Near indeed is his salvation to those who fear him, glory dwelling in our land.
2. Truth shall spring out of the earth, and justice shall look down from heaven.
3. Justice shall walk be - fore him, and prepare the way of his steps.

Gospel Acclamation for this celebration may be found on page 224.
A separate assembly response may be found on page 269.

SECOND SUNDAY OF ADVENT — C

Psalm 126: 1–2, 2–3, 4–5, 6 [6]

Gospel Acclamation for this celebration may be found on page 224.
A separate assembly response may be found on page 273.

THIRD SUNDAY OF ADVENT — A

Psalm 146: 6–7, 8–9, 9–10 [7]

RESPONSE: Cantor/All (♩ = *ca. 70*) [*or: Alleluia.*]

Lord,___ Lord,___ come___ and save us, come___ and save us.___

VERSES: Cantor or SATB

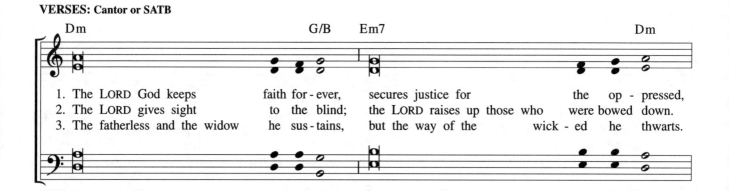

1. The LORD God keeps faith for - ever, secures justice for the op - pressed,
2. The LORD gives sight to the blind; the LORD raises up those who were bowed down.
3. The fatherless and the widow he sus - tains, but the way of the wick - ed he thwarts.

1. gives food to the hungry. The LORD sets cap - tives free.
2. The LORD loves the just; the LORD pro - tects strangers.
3. The LORD shall reign for - ever; your God, O Zion, through all gen - er - ations.

Gospel Acclamation for this celebration may be found on page 224.
A separate assembly response may be found on page 268.

THIRD SUNDAY OF ADVENT — B

Luke 1: 46–48, 49–50, 53–54 [8]

Gospel Acclamation for this celebration may be found on page 224.
A separate assembly response may be found on page 271.

THIRD SUNDAY OF ADVENT — C

Isaiah 12: 2–3, 4, 5–6 [9]

Gospel Acclamation for this celebration may be found on page 224.
A separate assembly response may be found on page 263.

FOURTH SUNDAY OF ADVENT — A

Psalm 24: 1–2, 3–4, 5–6 [10]

RESPONSE: Cantor/All (♩= ca. 90)

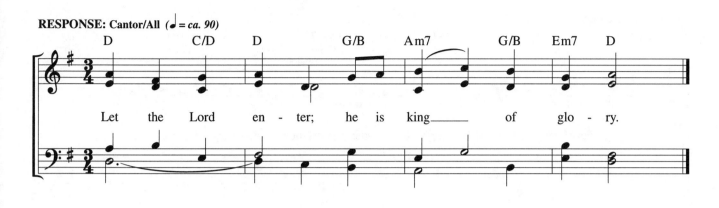

Let the Lord en-ter; he is king____ of glo-ry.

VERSES: Cantor or SATB

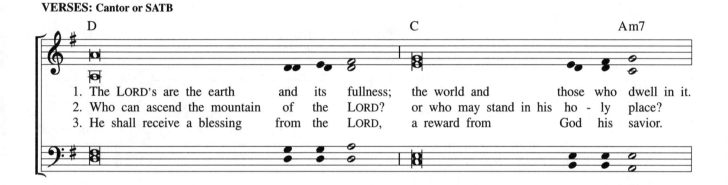

1. The LORD's are the earth and its fullness; the world and those who dwell in it.
2. Who can ascend the mountain of the LORD? or who may stand in his ho-ly place?
3. He shall receive a blessing from the LORD, a reward from God his savior.

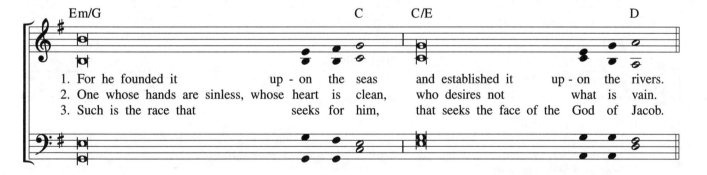

1. For he founded it up-on the seas and established it up-on the rivers.
2. One whose hands are sinless, whose heart is clean, who desires not what is vain.
3. Such is the race that seeks for him, that seeks the face of the God of Jacob.

Gospel Acclamation for this celebration may be found on page 224.
A separate assembly response may be found on page 267.

FOURTH SUNDAY OF ADVENT — B

Psalm 89: 2–3, 4–5, 27, 29 [11]

Gospel Acclamation for this celebration may be found on page 224.
A separate assembly response may be found on page 264.

FOURTH SUNDAY OF ADVENT — C

Psalm 80: 2–3, 15–16, 18–19 [12]

Gospel Acclamation for this celebration may be found on page 224.
A separate assembly response may be found on page 269.

NATIVITY OF THE LORD (CHRISTMAS): VIGIL MASS — ABC

Psalm 89: 4–5, 16–17, 27, 29 [13]

Gospel Acclamation for this celebration may be found on page 225.
A separate assembly response may be found on page 264.

NATIVITY OF THE LORD (CHRISTMAS): MASS AT MIDNIGHT — ABC

Psalm 96: 1–2, 2–3, 11–12, 13 [14]

Gospel Acclamation for this celebration may be found on page 225.
A separate assembly response may be found on page 276.

NATIVITY OF THE LORD (CHRISTMAS): MASS AT DAWN — ABC

Psalm 97: 1, 6, 11–12 [15]

Gospel Acclamation for this celebration may be found on page 225.
A separate assembly response may be found on page 262.

NATIVITY OF THE LORD (CHRISTMAS): MASS DURING THE DAY — ABC

Psalm 98: 1, 2–3, 3–4, 5–6 [16]

RESPONSE (♩. = ca. 45)

All the ends of the earth have seen the pow-er, the pow-er of God.

All the ends of the earth have seen the sav-ing pow-er of God.

VERSES: Cantor or SATB

1. Sing to the LORD a new song, for he has done won-drous deeds;
2. The LORD has made his salvation known: in the sight of the nations he has re-vealed his justice.
3. All the ends of the earth have seen the salvation by our God.
4. Sing praise to the LORD with the harp, with the harp and me-lo-dious song.

1. his right hand has won vic-t'ry for him, his ho-ly arm.
2. He has remembered his kindness and his faithfulness toward the house of Israel.
3. Sing joyfully to the LORD, all you lands; break into song; sing praise.
4. With trumpets and the sound of the horn sing joyfully before the King, the LORD.

Music © 2001, John Schiavone. Published by OCP Publications. All rights reserved.

Gospel Acclamation for this celebration may be found on page 225.
A separate assembly response may be found on page 262.

Holy Family of Jesus, Mary and Joseph — ABC

Psalm 128: 1–2, 3, 4–5 [17]

RESPONSE: Cantor/All (♩ = *ca. 110*)

Bless - ed are those___ who fear the Lord and walk in his ways.

VERSES: Cantor or SATB

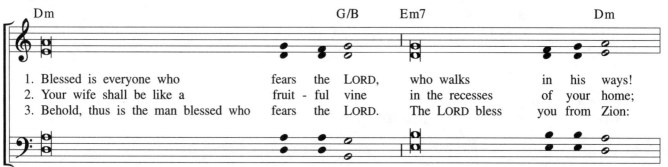

1. Blessed is everyone who fears the LORD, who walks in his ways!
2. Your wife shall be like a fruit - ful vine in the recesses of your home;
3. Behold, thus is the man blessed who fears the LORD. The LORD bless you from Zion:

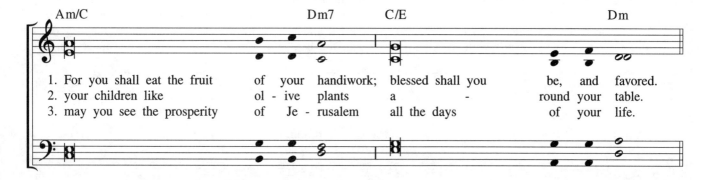

1. For you shall eat the fruit of your handiwork; blessed shall you be, and favored.
2. your children like ol - ive plants a - round your table.
3. may you see the prosperity of Je - rusalem all the days of your life.

Gospel Acclamation for this celebration may be found on page 226.
A separate assembly response may be found on page 263.

HOLY FAMILY OF JESUS, MARY AND JOSEPH — B
(Optional)

Psalm 105: 1–2, 3–4, 5–6, 8–9 [17]

RESPONSE: Cantor/All (♩ = ca. 70)

The Lord re-mem-bers his cov-e-nant for ev - er.

VERSES: Cantor or SATB

1. Give thanks to the LORD, in - voke his name; make known among the na - tions his deeds.
2. Glory in his ho - ly name; rejoice, O hearts that seek the LORD!
3. You descendants of Abra - ham, his servants, sons of Jacob, his cho - sen ones!
4. He remembers forev - er his covenant which he made binding for a thousand gen - er - ations

1. Sing to him, sing his praise, proclaim all his won - drous deeds.
2. Look to the LORD in his strength; constantly seek his face.
3. He, the LORD, is our God; throughout the earth his judg - ments pre - vail.
4. which he entered in - to with Abraham and by his oath to Isaac.

Gospel Acclamation for this celebration may be found on page 226.
A separate assembly response may be found on page 274.

HOLY FAMILY OF JESUS, MARY AND JOSEPH — C
(Optional)

Psalm 84: 2–3, 5–6, 9–10 [17]

RESPONSE: Cantor/All (♩ = ca. 95)

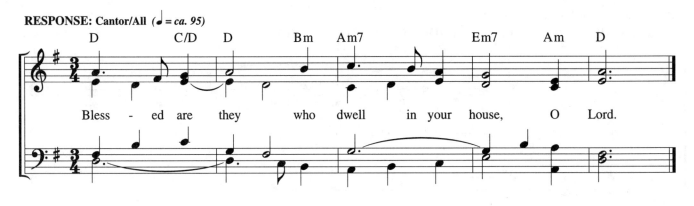

Bless - ed are they who dwell in your house, O Lord.

VERSES: Cantor or SATB

1. How lovely is your dwelling place, O LORD of hosts! My soul yearns and pines for the courts of the LORD.
2. Happy they who dwell in your house! Continual - ly they praise you.
3. O LORD of hosts, hear our prayer; hearken, O God of Jacob!

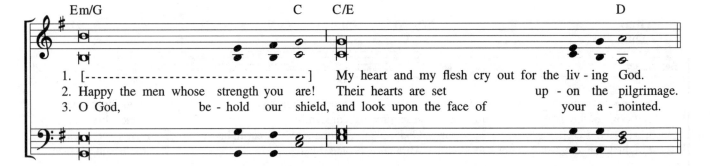

1. [------------------------------------] My heart and my flesh cry out for the liv - ing God.
2. Happy the men whose strength you are! Their hearts are set up - on the pilgrimage.
3. O God, be - hold our shield, and look upon the face of your a - nointed.

Gospel Acclamation for this celebration may be found on page 226.
A separate assembly response may be found on page 262.

BLESSED VIRGIN MARY, MOTHER OF GOD — ABC

Psalm 67: 2–3, 5, 6, 8 [18]

Gospel Acclamation for this celebration may be found on page 226.
A separate assembly response may be found on page 270.

SECOND SUNDAY AFTER CHRISTMAS — ABC

Psalm 147: 12–13, 14–15, 19–20 [19]

RESPONSE: Cantor/All (♩ = *ca. 70*) [*or:* Alleluia.]

The Word of God be-came man___ and lived a-mong___ us.___

VERSES: Cantor or SATB

1. Glorify the LORD, O Je - rusalem; praise your God, O Zion.
2. He has granted peace in your borders; with the best of wheat he fills you.
3. He has proclaimed his word to Jacob, his statutes and his ordinan - ces to Israel.

1. For he has strengthened the bars of your gates; he has blessed your chil - dren with-in you.
2. He sends forth his command to the earth; swiftly runs his word!
3. He has not done thus for any oth - er nation; his ordinances he has not made known to them. Al - le - luia.

Gospel Acclamation for this celebration may be found on page 226.
A separate assembly response may be found on page 276.

EPIPHANY OF THE LORD — ABC

Psalm 72: 1–2, 7–8, 10–11, 12–13 [20]

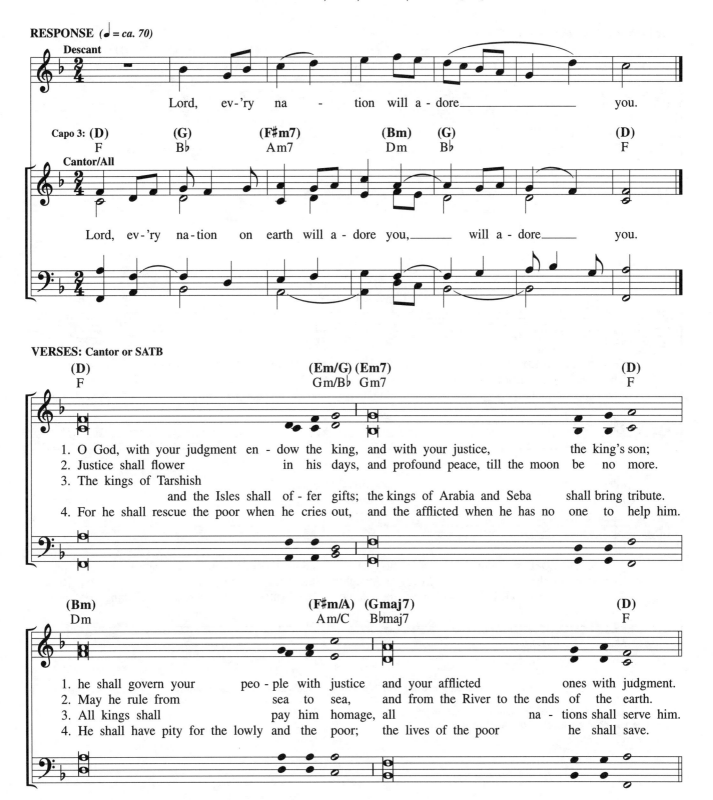

Gospel Acclamation for this celebration may be found on page 227.
A separate assembly response may be found on page 268.

Baptism of the Lord — ABC

Psalm 29: 1–2, 3–4, 3, 9–10 [21]

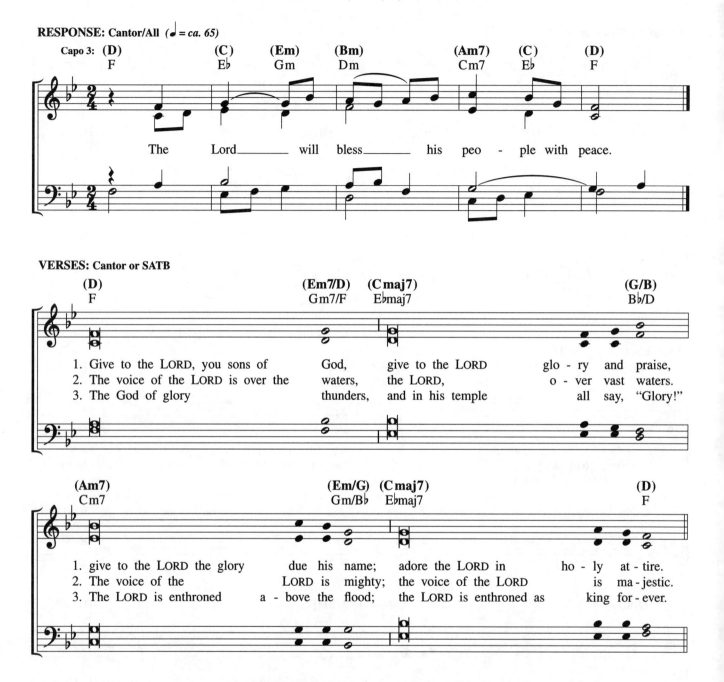

Gospel Acclamation for this celebration may be found on page 227.
A separate assembly response may be found on page 275.

BAPTISM OF THE LORD — B
(Optional)

Isaiah 12: 2–3, 4bcd, 5–6 [21]

RESPONSE: Cantor/All (♩ = ca. 105)

You will draw wa- ter joy- ful- ly from the springs of sal- va- tion.

VERSES: Cantor or SATB

1a. God indeed is my savior; I am confident and un - a - fraid. **(to 1b)**
1b. My strength and my courage is the LORD, and he has been my savior. **(to 1c)**
2. Give thanks to the LORD, ac - claim his name; among the nations make known his deeds,
3. Sing praise to the LORD for his glo - rious a - chievement; let this be known throughout all the earth.

1c. With joy you will draw water at the fountain of sal - vation.
2. [---] proclaim how exalted is his name.
3. Shout with exultation, O cit - y of Zion, for great in your midst is the Holy One of Israel!

Gospel Acclamation for this celebration may be found on page 227.
A separate assembly response may be found on page 277.

Baptism of the Lord — C
(Optional)

Psalm 104: 1b–2, 3–4, 24–25, 27–28, 29–30 [21]

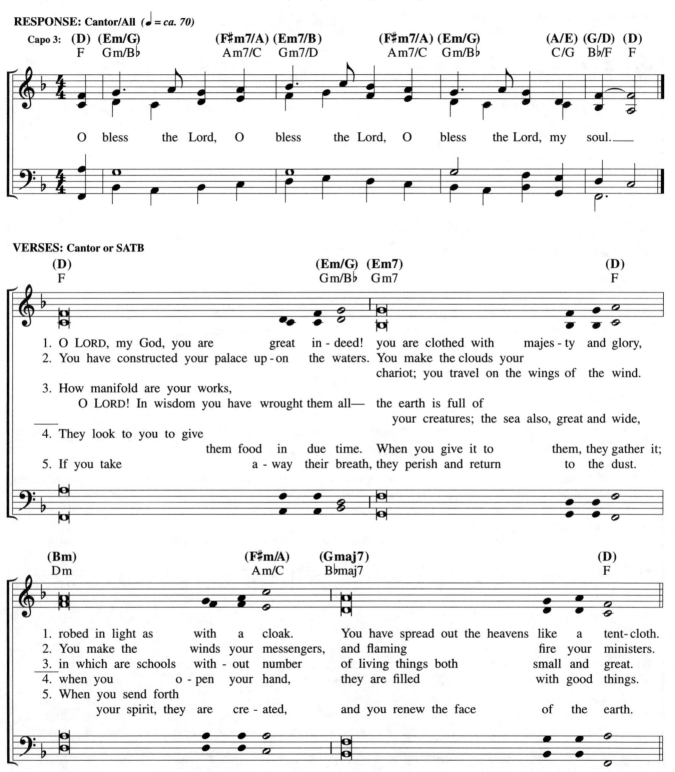

Gospel Acclamation for this celebration may be found on page 227.
A separate assembly response may be found on page 271.

ASH WEDNESDAY — ABC

Psalm 51: 3–4, 5–6ab, 12–13, 14 and 17 [219]

RESPONSE: Cantor/All (♩ = *ca. 55*)

Be mer-ci-ful, O Lord, for we have sinned.

VERSES: Cantor or SATB

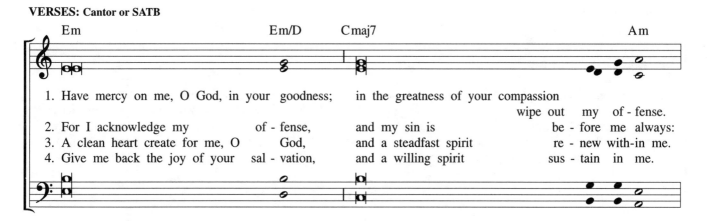

1. Have mercy on me, O God, in your goodness; in the greatness of your compassion wipe out my of-fense.
2. For I acknowledge my of-fense, and my sin is be-fore me always:
3. A clean heart create for me, O God, and a steadfast spirit re-new with-in me.
4. Give me back the joy of your sal-vation, and a willing spirit sus-tain in me.

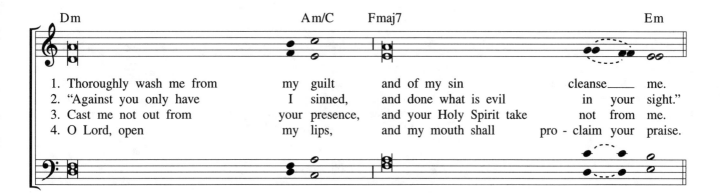

1. Thoroughly wash me from my guilt and of my sin cleanse me.
2. "Against you only have I sinned, and done what is evil in your sight."
3. Cast me not out from your presence, and your Holy Spirit take not from me.
4. O Lord, open my lips, and my mouth shall pro-claim your praise.

Gospel Acclamation for this celebration may be found on page 228.
A separate assembly response may be found on page 262.

FIRST SUNDAY OF LENT — A

Psalm 51: 3–4, 5–6, 12–13, 17 [22]

RESPONSE: Cantor/All (♩ = *ca. 55*)

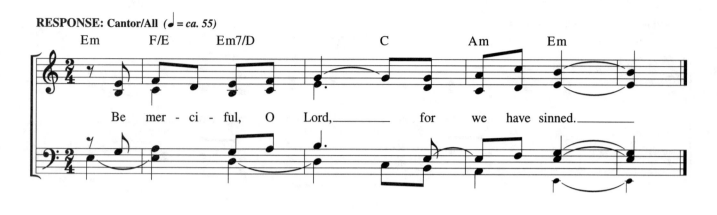

Be mer - ci - ful, O Lord,_____ for we have sinned._____

VERSES: Cantor or SATB

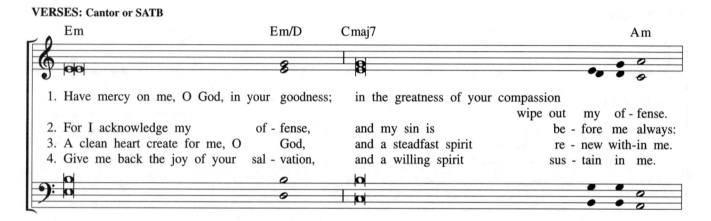

1. Have mercy on me, O God, in your goodness; in the greatness of your compassion wipe out my of - fense.
2. For I acknowledge my of - fense, and my sin is be - fore me always:
3. A clean heart create for me, O God, and a steadfast spirit re - new with-in me.
4. Give me back the joy of your sal - vation, and a willing spirit sus - tain in me.

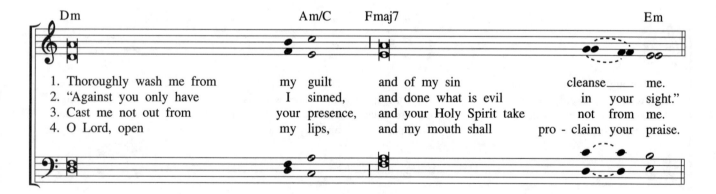

1. Thoroughly wash me from my guilt and of my sin cleanse_____ me.
2. "Against you only have I sinned, and done what is evil in your sight."
3. Cast me not out from your presence, and your Holy Spirit take not from me.
4. O Lord, open my lips, and my mouth shall pro - claim your praise.

Gospel Acclamation for this celebration may be found on page 228.
A separate assembly response may be found on page 262.

FIRST SUNDAY OF LENT — B

Psalm 25: 4–5, 6–7, 8–9 [23]

RESPONSE: Cantor/All (♩ = ca. 80)

Your ways, O Lord, are love and truth___ to those who keep your cov - e - nant.___

VERSES: Cantor or SATB

1. Your ways, O LORD, make known to me; teach me your paths.
2. Remember that your compas - sion, O LORD, and your love are from of old.
3. Good and upright is the LORD, thus he shows sin - ners the way.

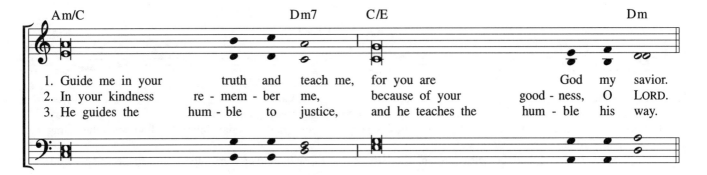

1. Guide me in your truth and teach me, for you are God my savior.
2. In your kindness re - mem - ber me, because of your good - ness, O LORD.
3. He guides the hum - ble to justice, and he teaches the hum - ble his way.

Gospel Acclamation for this celebration may be found on page 228.
A separate assembly response may be found on page 278.

FIRST SUNDAY OF LENT — C

Psalm 91: 1–2, 10–11, 12–13, 14–15 [24]

RESPONSE: Cantor/All (♩ = *ca. 90*)

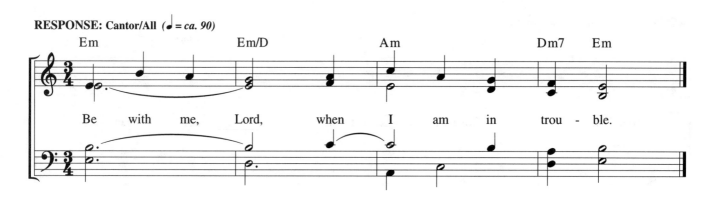

Be with me, Lord, when I am in trou - ble.

VERSES: Cantor or SATB

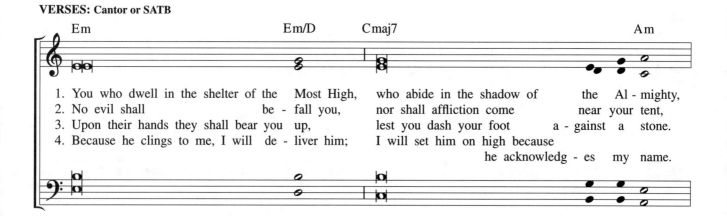

1. You who dwell in the shelter of the Most High, who abide in the shadow of the Al - mighty,
2. No evil shall be - fall you, nor shall affliction come near your tent,
3. Upon their hands they shall bear you up, lest you dash your foot a - gainst a stone.
4. Because he clings to me, I will de - liver him; I will set him on high because he acknowledg - es my name.

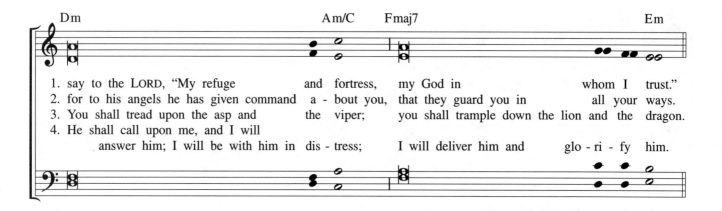

1. say to the LORD, "My refuge and fortress, my God in whom I trust."
2. for to his angels he has given command a - bout you, that they guard you in all your ways.
3. You shall tread upon the asp and the viper; you shall trample down the lion and the dragon.
4. He shall call upon me, and I will answer him; I will be with him in dis - tress; I will deliver him and glo - ri - fy him.

Gospel Acclamation for this celebration may be found on page 228.
A separate assembly response may be found on page 262.

SECOND SUNDAY OF LENT — A

Psalm 33: 4–5, 18–19, 20, 22 [25]

RESPONSE: Cantor/All (♩ = *ca. 85*)

Lord, let your mer-cy be on us,_____ as we place our trust in you._____

VERSES: Cantor or SATB

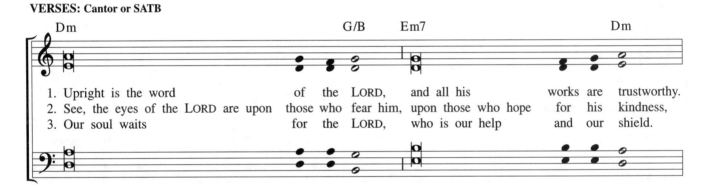

1. Upright is the word of the LORD, and all his works are trustworthy.
2. See, the eyes of the LORD are upon those who fear him, upon those who hope for his kindness,
3. Our soul waits for the LORD, who is our help and our shield.

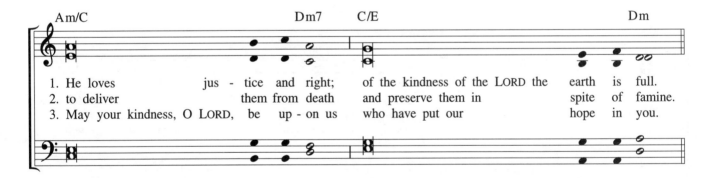

1. He loves jus-tice and right; of the kindness of the LORD the earth is full.
2. to deliver them from death and preserve them in spite of famine.
3. May your kindness, O LORD, be up-on us who have put our hope in you.

Gospel Acclamation for this celebration may be found on page 228.
A separate assembly response may be found on page 269.

SECOND SUNDAY OF LENT — B

Psalm 116: 10, 15, 16–17, 18–19 [26]

RESPONSE: Cantor/All (♩ = *ca. 80*)

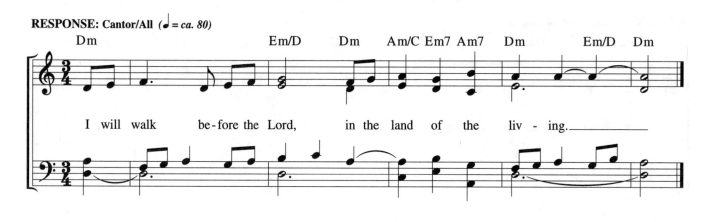

I will walk be-fore the Lord, in the land of the liv-ing._____

VERSES: Cantor or SATB

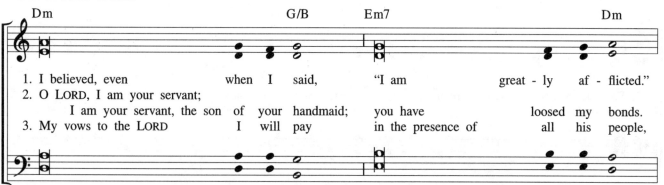

1. I believed, even when I said, "I am great - ly af - flicted."
2. O LORD, I am your servant;
   I am your servant, the son of your handmaid; you have loosed my bonds.
3. My vows to the LORD I will pay in the presence of all his people,

1. Precious in the eyes of the LORD is the death of his faithful ones.
2. To you will I offer sacrifice of thanks - giving, and I will call upon the name of the LORD.
3. in the courts of the house of the LORD, in your midst, O Je - rusalem.

Gospel Acclamation for this celebration may be found on page 228.
A separate assembly response may be found on page 266.

SECOND SUNDAY OF LENT — C

Psalm 27: 1, 7–8, 8–9, 13–14 [27]

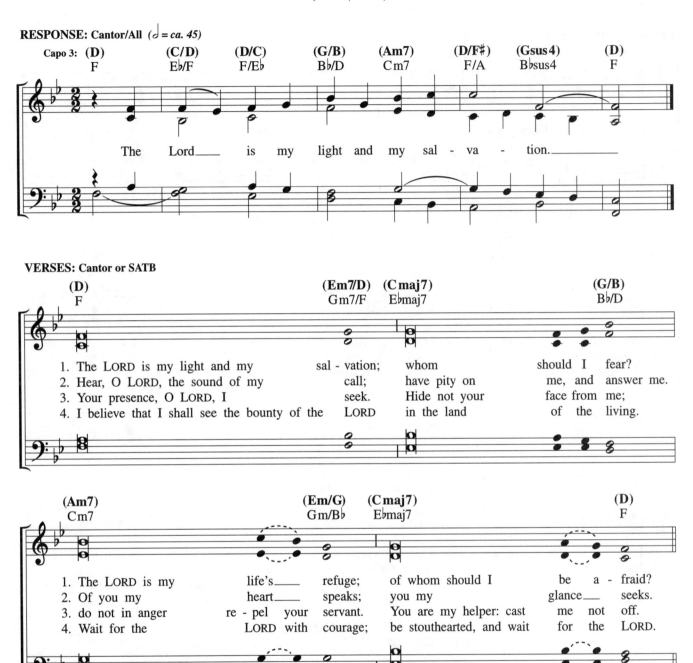

Gospel Acclamation for this celebration may be found on page 228.
A separate assembly response may be found on page 274.

THIRD SUNDAY OF LENT — A

Psalm 95: 1–2, 6–7, 8–9 [28]

RESPONSE: Cantor/All (♩ = ca. 45)

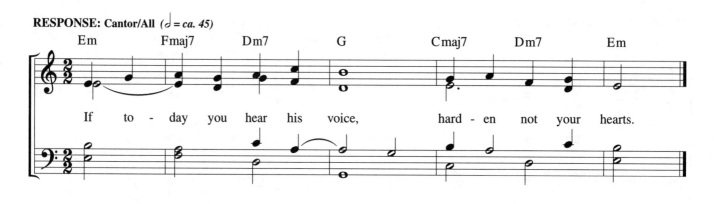

If to-day you hear his voice, hard-en not your hearts.

VERSES: Cantor or SATB

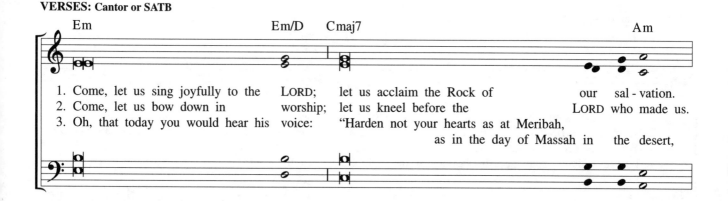

1. Come, let us sing joyfully to the LORD; let us acclaim the Rock of our sal-vation.
2. Come, let us bow down in worship; let us kneel before the LORD who made us.
3. Oh, that today you would hear his voice: "Harden not your hearts as at Meribah, as in the day of Massah in the desert,

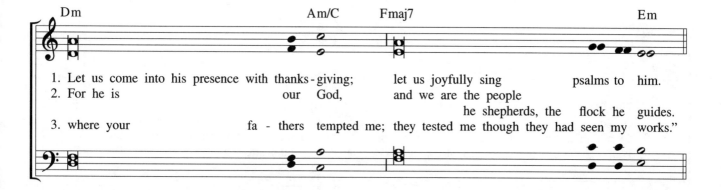

1. Let us come into his presence with thanks-giving; let us joyfully sing psalms to him.
2. For he is our God, and we are the people he shepherds, the flock he guides.
3. where your fa-thers tempted me; they tested me though they had seen my works."

Gospel Acclamation for this celebration may be found on page 229.
A separate assembly response may be found on page 266.

THIRD SUNDAY OF LENT — B

Psalm 19: 8, 9, 10, 11 [29]

RESPONSE: Cantor/All (♩ = ca. 50)

Lord, you have the words of ev - er - last - ing life.

VERSES: Cantor or SATB

1. The law of the LORD is perfect, refresh - ing the soul;
2. The precepts of the LORD are right, rejoic - ing the heart;
3. The fear of the LORD is pure, endur - ing for - ever;
4. They are more pre - cious than gold, than a heap of pur - est gold;

1. the decree of the LORD is trustworthy, giving wisdom to the simple.
2. the command of the LORD is clear, enlighten - ing the eye.
3. the ordinances of the LORD are true, all of them just.
4. sweeter al - so than syrup or honey from the comb.

Gospel Acclamation for this celebration may be found on page 229.
A separate assembly response may be found on page 270.

Note: When celebrating the R.C.I.A., the Responsorial Psalm from Year A may be used (page 40).

THIRD SUNDAY OF LENT — C

Psalm 103: 1–2, 3–4, 6–7, 8, 11 [30]

Gospel Acclamation for this celebration may be found on page 229.
A separate assembly response may be found on page 274.

Note: When celebrating the R.C.I.A., the Responsorial Psalm from Year A may be used (page 40).

FOURTH SUNDAY OF LENT — A

Psalm 23: 1–3a, 3b–4, 5, 6 [31]

RESPONSE: Cantor/All (♩. = ca. 40)

The Lord_____ is my shep-herd; there is noth-ing I shall want._____

VERSES: Cantor or SATB

1. The LORD is my shepherd; I shall not want. In verdant pastures he gives me re-pose;
2. He guides me in right paths for his name's sake. Even though I walk in the dark valley I fear no evil;
3. You spread the table be-fore me in the sight of my foes;
4. Only goodness and kindness follow me all the days of my life;

1. beside restful wa-ters he leads me; he refreshes my soul.
2. for you are at my side with your rod and your staff that give me courage.
3. you anoint my head with oil; my cup over-flows.
4. and I shall dwell in the house of the LORD for years to come.

Gospel Acclamation for this celebration may be found on page 229.
A separate assembly response may be found on page 274.

FOURTH SUNDAY OF LENT — B

Psalm 137: 1–2, 3, 4–5, 6 [32]

RESPONSE: Cantor/All (♩ = *ca. 45*)

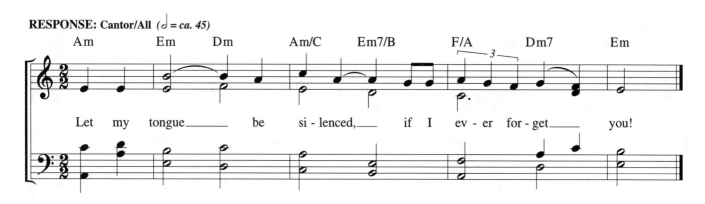

Let my tongue___ be si - lenced,___ if I ev - er for - get___ you!

VERSES: Cantor or SATB

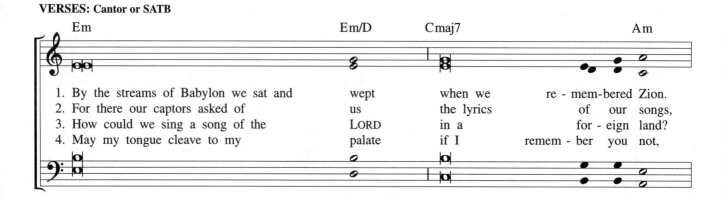

1. By the streams of Babylon we sat and wept when we re - mem-bered Zion.
2. For there our captors asked of us the lyrics of our songs,
3. How could we sing a song of the LORD in a for - eign land?
4. May my tongue cleave to my palate if I remem - ber you not,

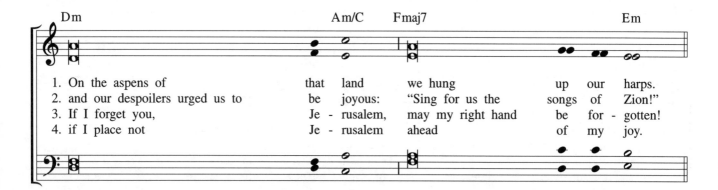

1. On the aspens of that land we hung up our harps.
2. and our despoilers urged us to be joyous: "Sing for us the songs of Zion!"
3. If I forget you, Je - rusalem, may my right hand be for - gotten!
4. if I place not Je - rusalem ahead of my joy.

Gospel Acclamation for this celebration may be found on page 229.
A separate assembly response may be found on page 267.

Note: When celebrating the R.C.I.A., the Responsorial Psalm from Year A may be used (page 43).

FOURTH SUNDAY OF LENT — C

Psalm 34: 2–3, 4–5, 6–7 [33]

RESPONSE: Cantor/All (♩. = *ca.* 35)

Taste and see, taste and see the good-ness of the Lord.

VERSES: Cantor or SATB

1. I will bless the LORD at all times; his praise shall be ever in my mouth.
2. Glorify the LORD with me, let us together ex-tol his name.
3. Look to him that you may be ra-diant with joy, and your faces may not blush with shame.

1. Let my soul glory in the LORD; the lowly will hear me and be glad.
2. I sought the LORD, and he answered me and delivered me from all my fears.
3. When the poor one called out, the LORD heard, and from all his dis-tress he saved him.

Gospel Acclamation for this celebration may be found on page 229.
A separate assembly response may be found on page 272.

Note: When celebrating the R.C.I.A., the Responsorial Psalm from Year A may be used (page 43).

FIFTH SUNDAY OF LENT — A

Psalm 130: 1–2, 3–4, 5–6, 7–8 [34]

Gospel Acclamation for this celebration may be found on page 230.
A separate assembly response may be found on page 277.

FIFTH SUNDAY OF LENT — B

Psalm 51: 3–4, 12–13, 14–15 [35]

RESPONSE: Cantor/All (♩ = *ca. 90*)

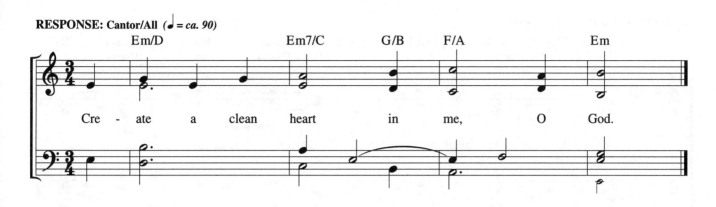

Cre - ate a clean heart in me, O God.

VERSES: Cantor or SATB

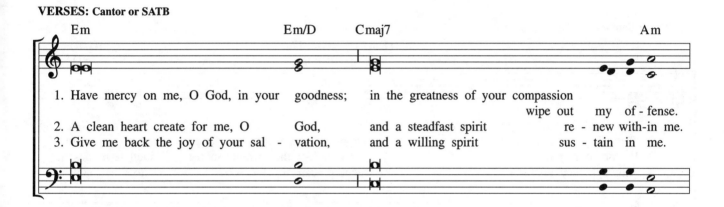

1. Have mercy on me, O God, in your goodness; in the greatness of your compassion wipe out my of - fense.
2. A clean heart create for me, O God, and a steadfast spirit re - new with-in me.
3. Give me back the joy of your sal - vation, and a willing spirit sus - tain in me.

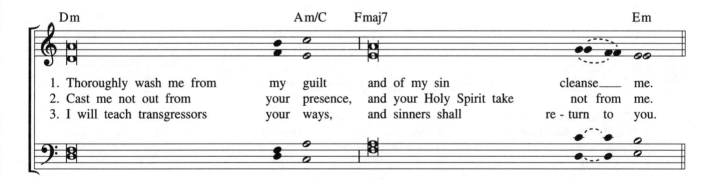

1. Thoroughly wash me from my guilt and of my sin cleanse____ me.
2. Cast me not out from your presence, and your Holy Spirit take not from me.
3. I will teach transgressors your ways, and sinners shall re - turn to you.

Gospel Acclamation for this celebration may be found on page 230.
A separate assembly response may be found on page 263.

Note: When celebrating the R.C.I.A., the Responsorial Psalm from Year A may be used (page 46).

FIFTH SUNDAY OF LENT — C

Psalm 126: 1–2, 2–3, 4–5, 6 [36]

Gospel Acclamation for this celebration may be found on page 230.
A separate assembly response may be found on page 273.

Note: When celebrating the R.C.I.A., the Responsorial Psalm from Year A may be used (page 46).

PALM SUNDAY OF THE LORD'S PASSION — ABC

Psalm 22: 8–9, 17–18, 19–20, 23–24 [38]

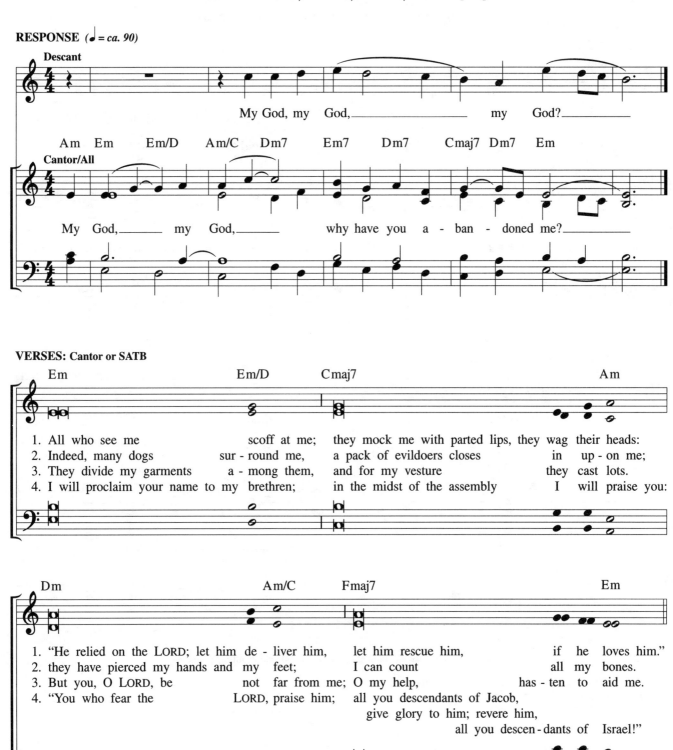

RESPONSE (♩ = ca. 90)

Descant: My God, my God,_____ my God?_____

Am Em Em/D Am/C Dm7 Em7 Dm7 Cmaj7 Dm7 Em

Cantor/All: My God,_____ my God,_____ why have you a-ban-doned me?_____

VERSES: Cantor or SATB

Em | Em/D | Cmaj7 | Am

1. All who see me scoff at me; they mock me with parted lips, they wag their heads:
2. Indeed, many dogs sur-round me, a pack of evildoers closes in up-on me;
3. They divide my garments a-mong them, and for my vesture they cast lots.
4. I will proclaim your name to my brethren; in the midst of the assembly I will praise you:

Dm | Am/C | Fmaj7 | Em

1. "He relied on the LORD; let him de-liver him, let him rescue him, if he loves him."
2. they have pierced my hands and my feet; I can count all my bones.
3. But you, O LORD, be not far from me; O my help, has-ten to aid me.
4. "You who fear the LORD, praise him; all you descendants of Jacob, give glory to him; revere him, all you descen-dants of Israel!"

Gospel Acclamation for this celebration may be found on page 230.
A separate assembly response may be found on page 270.

HOLY THURSDAY:
EVENING MASS OF THE LORD'S SUPPER — ABC

Psalm 116: 12–13, 15–16bc, 17–18 [39]

Gospel Acclamation for this celebration may be found on page 230.
A separate assembly response may be found on page 271.

VERSES: Cantor or SATB

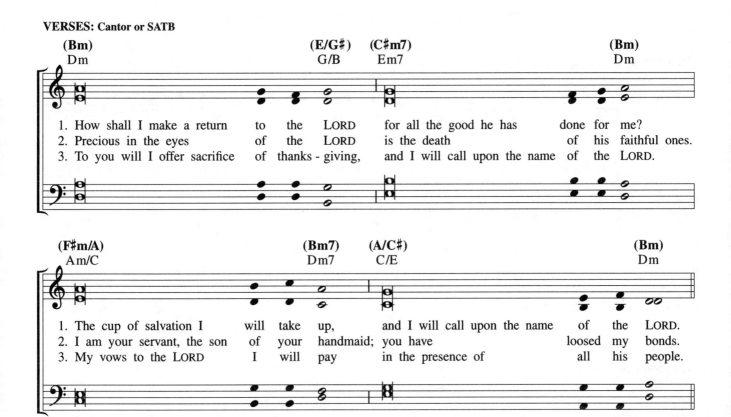

1. How shall I make a return to the LORD for all the good he has done for me?
2. Precious in the eyes of the LORD is the death of his faithful ones.
3. To you will I offer sacrifice of thanks-giving, and I will call upon the name of the LORD.

1. The cup of salvation I will take up, and I will call upon the name of the LORD.
2. I am your servant, the son of your handmaid; you have loosed my bonds.
3. My vows to the LORD I will pay in the presence of all his people.

GOOD FRIDAY OF THE LORD'S PASSION — ABC

Psalm 31: 2, 6, 12–13, 15–16, 17, 25 [40]

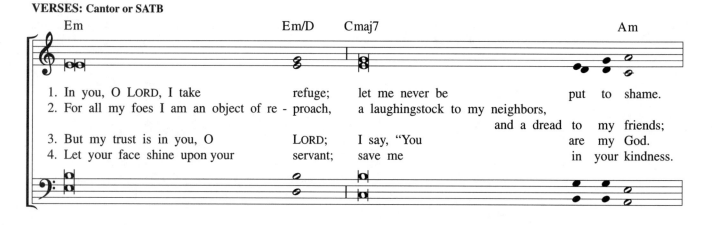

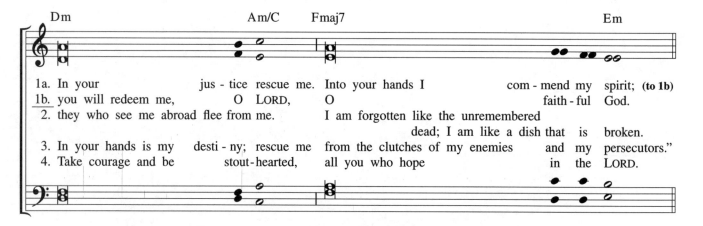

Gospel Acclamation for this celebration may be found on page 230.
A separate assembly response may be found on page 263.

Easter Vigil — ABC

Psalm 104: 1–2, 5–6, 10, 12, 13–14, 24, 35 [41]

Responsorial Psalm following the first reading:

RESPONSE: Cantor/All (♩. = *ca. 40*)

Lord,___ send out your Spir-it, and re - new the face of the earth.

VERSES: Cantor or SATB

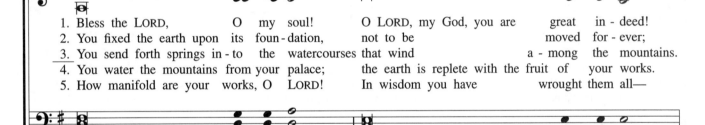

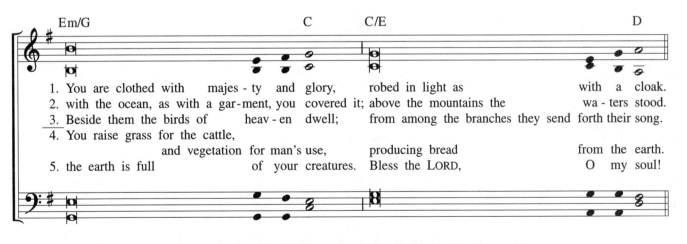

1. Bless the LORD, O my soul! O LORD, my God, you are great in - deed!
2. You fixed the earth upon its foun - dation, not to be moved for - ever;
3. You send forth springs in - to the watercourses that wind a - mong the mountains.
4. You water the mountains from your palace; the earth is replete with the fruit of your works.
5. How manifold are your works, O LORD! In wisdom you have wrought them all—

1. You are clothed with majes - ty and glory, robed in light as with a cloak.
2. with the ocean, as with a gar - ment, you covered it; above the mountains the wa - ters stood.
3. Beside them the birds of heav - en dwell; from among the branches they send forth their song.
4. You raise grass for the cattle, and vegetation for man's use, producing bread from the earth.
5. the earth is full of your creatures. Bless the LORD, O my soul!

A separate assembly response may be found on page 269.

EASTER VIGIL — ABC

Psalm 33: 4–5, 6–7, 12–13, 20–22 [41]

OR
Responsorial Psalm following the first reading:

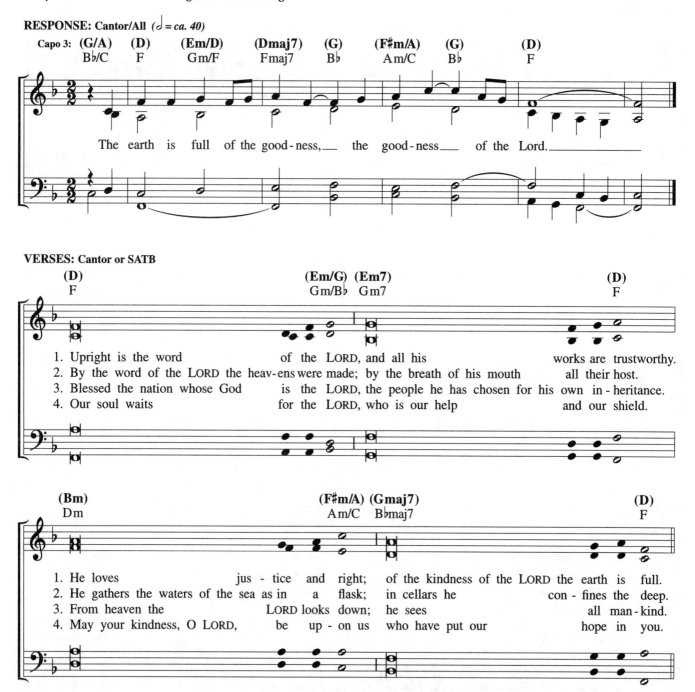

A separate assembly response may be found on page 273.

EASTER VIGIL — ABC

Psalm 16: 5, 8, 9–10, 11 [41]

Responsorial Psalm following the second reading:

RESPONSE: Cantor/All (♩ = ca. 95)

You are my in-her-i-tance, O Lord._____

VERSES: Cantor or SATB

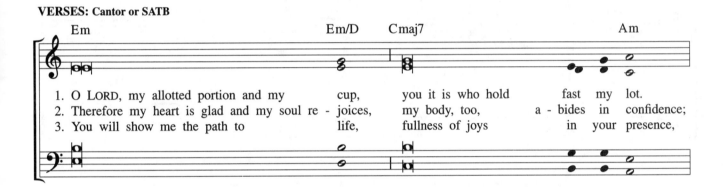

1. O LORD, my allotted portion and my cup, you it is who hold fast my lot.
2. Therefore my heart is glad and my soul re-joices, my body, too, a-bides in confidence;
3. You will show me the path to life, fullness of joys in your presence,

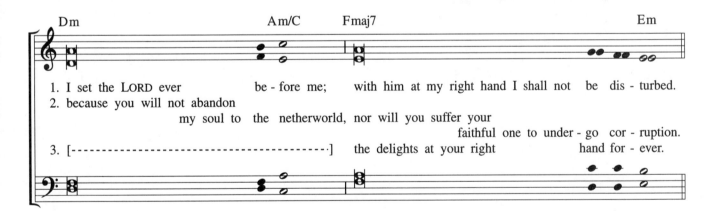

1. I set the LORD ever be-fore me; with him at my right hand I shall not be dis-turbed.
2. because you will not abandon my soul to the netherworld, nor will you suffer your faithful one to under-go cor-ruption.
3. [------------------------------] the delights at your right hand for-ever.

Music © 2001 , John Schiavone. Published by OCP Publications. All rights reserved.

A separate assembly response may be found on page 277.

EASTER VIGIL — ABC

Exodus 15: 1–2, 3–4, 5–6, 17–18 [41]

Responsorial Psalm following the third reading:

RESPONSE: Cantor/All (♩ = *ca. 100*)

Let us sing to the Lord; he has cov-ered him-self

in___ glo - ry, in___ glo - ry.

A separate assembly response may be found on page 268.

VERSES: Cantor or SATB

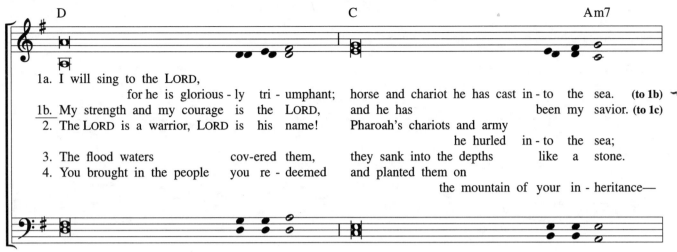

1a. I will sing to the LORD,
  for he is glorious-ly tri-umphant; horse and chariot he has cast in-to the sea. **(to 1b)** →

1b. My strength and my courage is the LORD, and he has been my savior. **(to 1c)**

2. The LORD is a warrior, LORD is his name! Pharoah's chariots and army
  he hurled in-to the sea;

3. The flood waters cov-ered them, they sank into the depths like a stone.

4. You brought in the people you re-deemed and planted them on
  the mountain of your in-heritance—

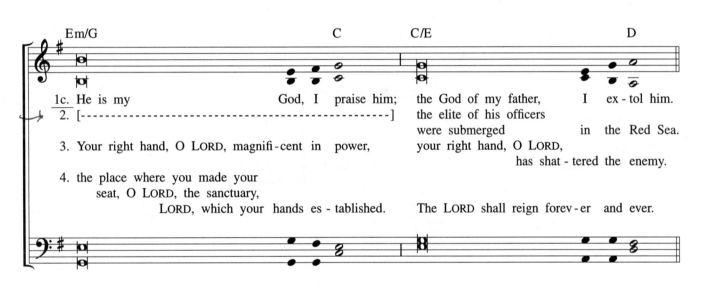

1c. He is my God, I praise him; the God of my father, I ex-tol him.

2. [---] the elite of his officers
  were submerged in the Red Sea.

3. Your right hand, O LORD, magnifi-cent in power, your right hand, O LORD,
  has shat-tered the enemy.

4. the place where you made your
  seat, O LORD, the sanctuary,
  LORD, which your hands es-tablished. The LORD shall reign forev-er and ever.

EASTER VIGIL — ABC

Psalm 30: 2, 4, 5–6, 11–12, 13 [41]

Responsorial Psalm following the fourth reading:

RESPONSE: Cantor/All (♩ = *ca. 75*)

I will praise you, Lord, for you have res - cued me.

VERSES: Cantor or SATB

1. I will extol you, O LORD, for you drew me clear and did not let my enemies rejoice o - ver me.
2a. Sing praise to the LORD, you his faith-ful ones, and give thanks to his ho - ly name. **(to 2b)**
2b. For his anger lasts but a moment; a lifetime, his good will. **(to 2c)**
3. Hear, O LORD, and have pit - y on me; O LORD, be my helper.

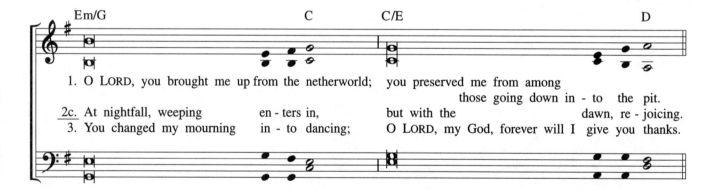

1. O LORD, you brought me up from the netherworld; you preserved me from among those going down in - to the pit.
2c. At nightfall, weeping en - ters in, but with the dawn, re - joicing.
3. You changed my mourning in - to dancing; O LORD, my God, forever will I give you thanks.

A separate assembly response may be found on page 266.

EASTER VIGIL — ABC

Isaiah 12: 2–3, 4, 5–6 [41]

Responsorial Psalm following the fifth reading:

A separate assembly response may be found on page 277.

EASTER VIGIL — ABC

Psalm 19: 8, 9, 10, 11 [41]

Responsorial Psalm following the sixth reading:

A separate assembly response may be found on page 270.

EASTER VIGIL — ABC

Psalm 42: 3, 5; 43: 3, 4 [41]

Responsorial Psalm following the seventh reading (when baptism is celebrated):

A separate assembly response may be found on page 268.

EASTER VIGIL — ABC

Isaiah 12: 2–3, 4bcd, 5–6 [41]

Responsorial Psalm following the seventh reading (when baptism is not celebrated):

RESPONSE: Cantor/All (♩ = ca. 105)

You will draw wa - ter____ joy - ful - ly____ from the springs of sal - va - tion.____

VERSES: Cantor or SATB

1a. God indeed is my savior; I am confident and un - a - fraid. **(to 1b)**
1b. My strength and my courage is the LORD, and he has been my savior. **(to 1c)**
2. Give thanks to the LORD, ac - claim his name; among the nations make known his deeds,
3. Sing praise to the LORD for his glo - rious a - chievement; let this be known throughout all the earth.

1c. With joy you will draw water at the fountain of sal - vation.
2. [-------------------------------------] proclaim how exalted is his name.
3. Shout with exultation, O cit - y of Zion, for great in your midst is the Holy One of Israel!

A separate assembly response may be found on page 277.

EASTER VIGIL — ABC

Psalm 51: 12–13, 14–15, 18–19 [41]

OR

Responsorial Psalm following the seventh reading (when baptism is not celebrated):

RESPONSE: Cantor/All (♩ = *ca. 90*)

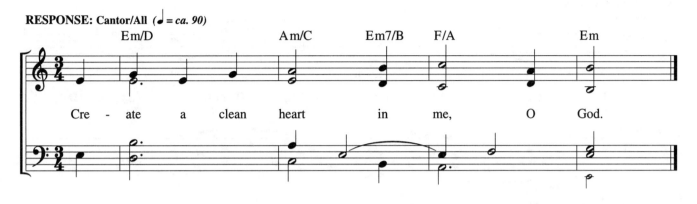

Cre - ate a clean heart in me, O God.

VERSES: Cantor or SATB

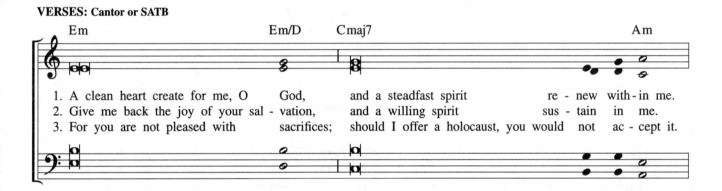

1. A clean heart create for me, O God, and a steadfast spirit re - new with - in me.
2. Give me back the joy of your sal - vation, and a willing spirit sus - tain in me.
3. For you are not pleased with sacrifices; should I offer a holocaust, you would not ac - cept it.

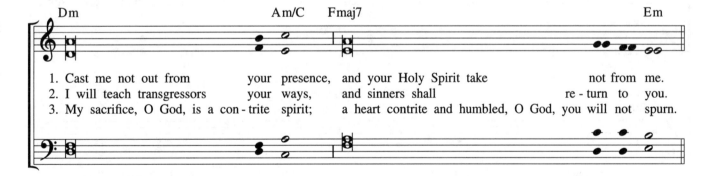

1. Cast me not out from your presence, and your Holy Spirit take not from me.
2. I will teach transgressors your ways, and sinners shall re - turn to you.
3. My sacrifice, O God, is a con - trite spirit; a heart contrite and humbled, O God, you will not spurn.

A separate assembly response may be found on page 263.

EASTER VIGIL — ABC

Psalm 118: 1–2, 16–17, 22–23 [41]

Responsorial Psalm following the Epistle:

*"After the Epistle has been read, all rise, and the priest solemnly intones the Alleluia three times, raising his voice a step each time. All repeat the alleluia each time. If necessary, the psalmist intones the Alleluia." (*Missale Romanum, editio typica tertia,* EV, no. 34)

A separate assembly response may be found on page 262.

EASTER SUNDAY — ABC
Commemoration of the Lord's Resurrection
Psalm 118: 1–2, 16–17, 22–23 [42]

Gospel Acclamation for this celebration may be found on page 232.
A separate assembly response may be found on page 276.

SECOND SUNDAY OF EASTER — ABC
Divine Mercy Sunday

Psalm 118: 2–4, 13–15, 22–24 [43, 44, 45]

RESPONSE: Cantor/All (♩. = *ca. 35*) [*or:* Alleluia.]

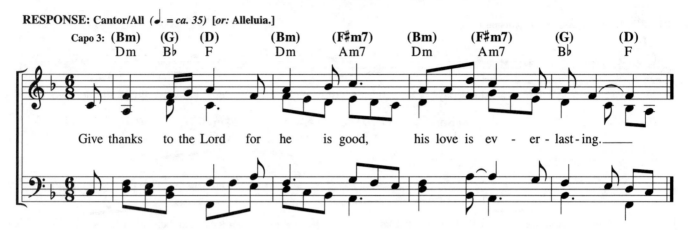

Give thanks to the Lord for he is good, his love is ev - er - last - ing.

Gospel Acclamation for this celebration may be found on page 232.
A separate assembly response may be found on page 264.

VERSES: Cantor or SATB

THIRD SUNDAY OF EASTER — A

Psalm 16: 1–2, 5, 7–8, 9–10, 11 [46]

RESPONSE: Cantor/All (♩ = ca. 45) [*or: Alleluia.*]

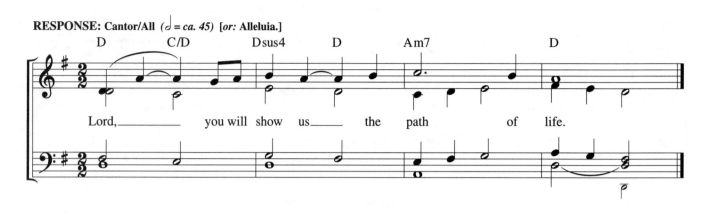

Lord, you will show us the path of life.

VERSES: Cantor or SATB

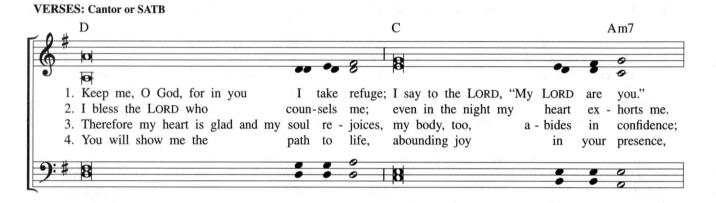

1. Keep me, O God, for in you I take refuge; I say to the LORD, "My LORD are you."
2. I bless the LORD who coun-sels me; even in the night my heart ex - horts me.
3. Therefore my heart is glad and my soul re - joices, my body, too, a - bides in confidence;
4. You will show me the path to life, abounding joy in your presence,

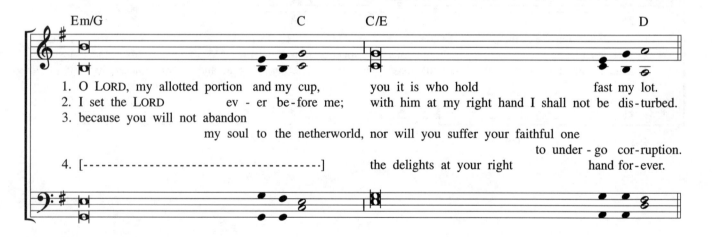

1. O LORD, my allotted portion and my cup, you it is who hold fast my lot.
2. I set the LORD ev - er be-fore me; with him at my right hand I shall not be dis-turbed.
3. because you will not abandon my soul to the netherworld, nor will you suffer your faithful one to under - go cor-ruption.
4. [-------------------------------------] the delights at your right hand for-ever.

Gospel Acclamation for this celebration may be found on page 232.
A separate assembly response may be found on page 270.

THIRD SUNDAY OF EASTER — B

Psalm 4: 2, 4, 7–8, 9 [47]

RESPONSE: Cantor/All (♩ = *ca. 40*) [*or: Alleluia.*]

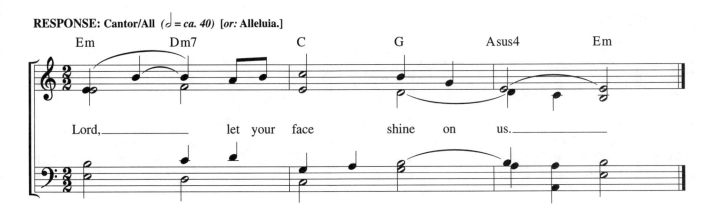

Lord,_____ let your face shine on us._____

VERSES: Cantor or SATB

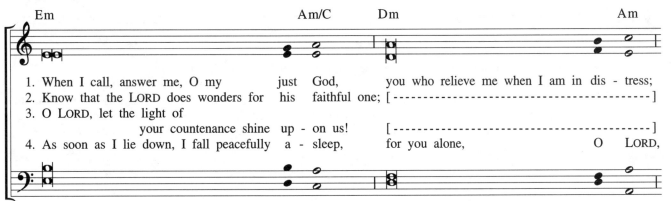

1. When I call, answer me, O my just God, you who relieve me when I am in dis - tress;
2. Know that the LORD does wonders for his faithful one; [- -]
3. O LORD, let the light of
   your countenance shine up - on us! [- -]
4. As soon as I lie down, I fall peacefully a - sleep, for you alone, O LORD,

1. have pity on me, and hear my prayer!
2. the LORD will hear me when I call up - on him.
3. You put gladness in - to my heart.
4. bring security to my dwelling.

Gospel Acclamation for this celebration may be found on page 232.
A separate assembly response may be found on page 269.

THIRD SUNDAY OF EASTER — C

Psalm 30: 2, 4, 5–6, 11–12, 13 [48]

RESPONSE: Cantor/All (♩ = *ca. 75*) [*or: Alleluia.*]

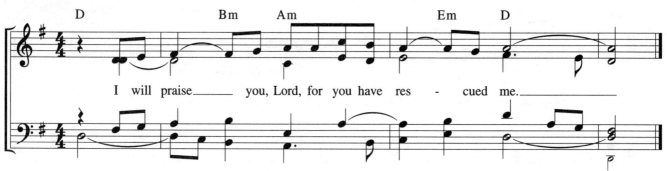

I will praise_____ you, Lord, for you have res - cued me._____

VERSES: Cantor or SATB

1. I will extol you, O LORD, for you drew me clear   and did not let my
                                                              enemies rejoice o - ver me.
2a. Sing praise to the LORD, you his   faith-ful ones,   and give thanks to his   ho - ly name. **(to 2b)**
2b. For his anger lasts   but a   moment; a lifetime,   his good will. **(to 2c)**
3. Hear, O LORD, and have   pit - y on me;   O LORD,   be my helper.

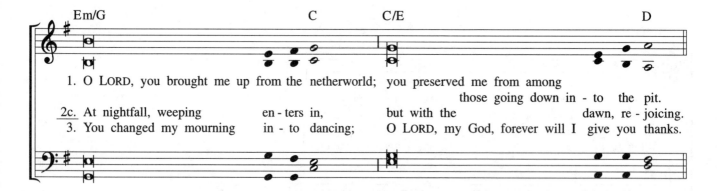

1. O LORD, you brought me up from the netherworld; you preserved me from among
                                                              those going down in - to   the pit.
2c. At nightfall, weeping   en - ters in,   but with the   dawn, re - joicing.
3. You changed my mourning   in - to dancing;   O LORD, my God, forever will I give you thanks.

Gospel Acclamation for this celebration may be found on page 232.
A separate assembly response may be found on page 266.

FOURTH SUNDAY OF EASTER — A

Psalm 23: 1–3a, 3b–4, 5, 6 [49]

RESPONSE: Cantor/All (♩. = *ca. 40*) [*or:* Alleluia.]

The Lord_____ is my shep-herd; there is noth - ing I shall want._____

VERSES: Cantor or SATB

1. The LORD is my shepherd; I shall not want. In verdant pastures he gives me re - pose;
2. He guides me in right paths for his name's sake. Even though I walk in the dark valley I fear no evil;
3. You spread the table be - fore me in the sight of my foes;
4. Only goodness and kindness follow me all the days of my life;

1. beside restful wa - ters he leads me; he refreshes my soul.
2. for you are at my side with your rod and your staff that give me courage.
3. you anoint my head with oil; my cup over - flows.
4. and I shall dwell in the house of the LORD for years to come.

Gospel Acclamation for this celebration may be found on page 233.
A separate assembly response may be found on page 274.

FOURTH SUNDAY OF EASTER — B

Psalm 118: 1, 8–9, 21–23, 26, 28, 29 [50]

Gospel Acclamation for this celebration may be found on page 233.
A separate assembly response may be found on page 275.

FOURTH SUNDAY OF EASTER — C

Psalm 100: 1–2, 3, 5 [51]

Gospel Acclamation for this celebration may be found on page 233.
A separate assembly response may be found on page 277.

FIFTH SUNDAY OF EASTER — A

Psalm 33: 1–2, 4–5, 18–19 [52]

RESPONSE: Cantor/All (♩ = *ca. 85*) [*or: Alleluia.*]

Lord, let your mer-cy be on us, _____ as we place our trust in you. ____

VERSES: Cantor or SATB

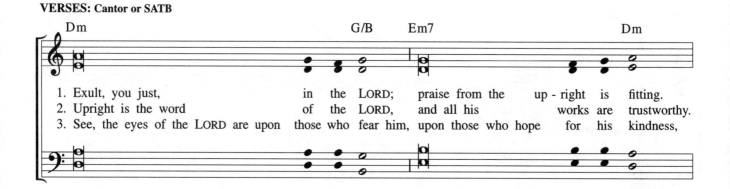

1. Exult, you just, in the LORD; praise from the up-right is fitting.
2. Upright is the word of the LORD, and all his works are trustworthy.
3. See, the eyes of the LORD are upon those who fear him, upon those who hope for his kindness,

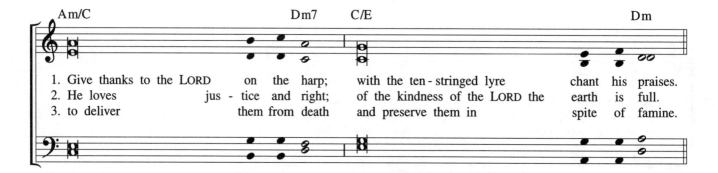

1. Give thanks to the LORD on the harp; with the ten-stringed lyre chant his praises.
2. He loves jus-tice and right; of the kindness of the LORD the earth is full.
3. to deliver them from death and preserve them in spite of famine.

Gospel Acclamation for this celebration may be found on page 233.
A separate assembly response may be found on page 269.

Fifth Sunday of Easter — B

Psalm 22: 26–27, 28, 30, 31–32 [53]

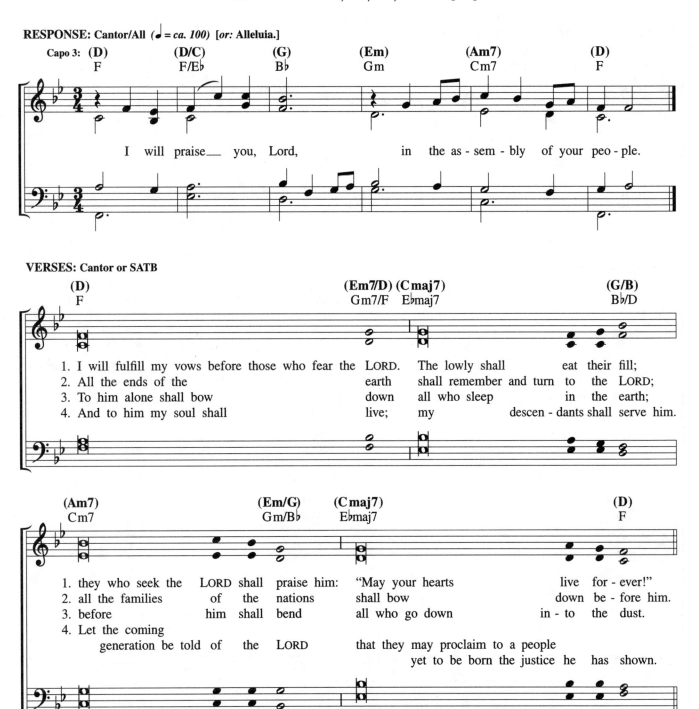

Gospel Acclamation for this celebration may be found on page 233.
A separate assembly response may be found on page 266.

FIFTH SUNDAY OF EASTER — C

Psalm 145: 8–9, 10–11, 12–13 [54]

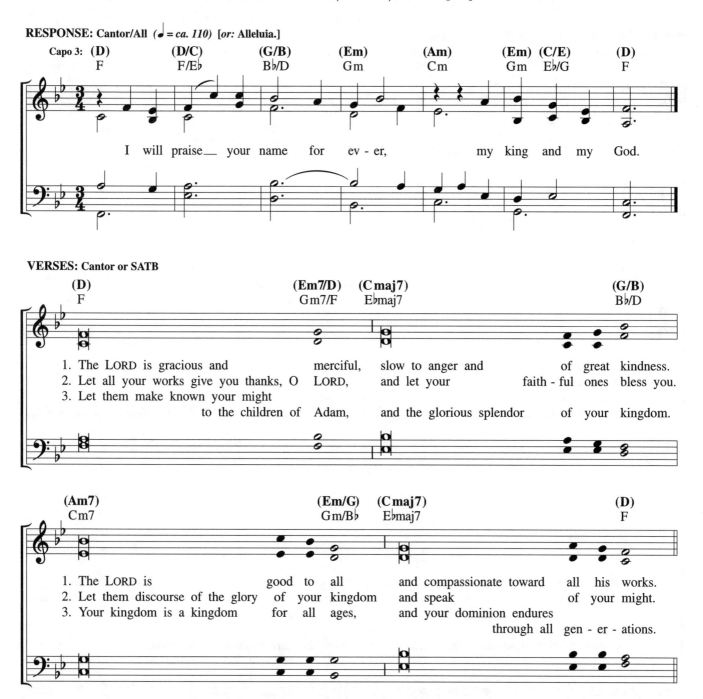

RESPONSE: Cantor/All (♩ = *ca. 110*) [*or:* Alleluia.]

I will praise your name for ev-er, my king and my God.

VERSES: Cantor or SATB

1. The LORD is gracious and merciful, slow to anger and of great kindness.
2. Let all your works give you thanks, O LORD, and let your faith-ful ones bless you.
3. Let them make known your might to the children of Adam, and the glorious splendor of your kingdom.

1. The LORD is good to all and compassionate toward all his works.
2. Let them discourse of the glory of your kingdom and speak of your might.
3. Your kingdom is a kingdom for all ages, and your dominion endures through all gen-er-ations.

Gospel Acclamation for this celebration may be found on page 233.
A separate assembly response may be found on page 266.

SIXTH SUNDAY OF EASTER — A

Psalm 66: 1–3, 4–5, 6–7, 16, 20 [55]

RESPONSE: Cantor/All (♩ = ca. 65) [*or:* Alleluia.]

Let all the earth _____ cry out to God with joy. _____

VERSES: Cantor or SATB

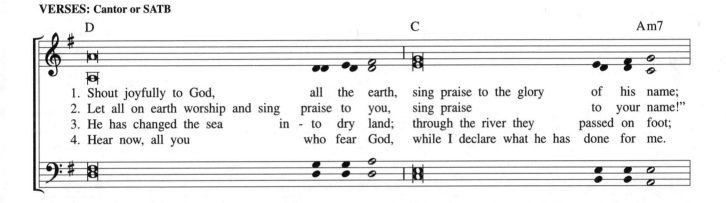

1. Shout joyfully to God, all the earth, sing praise to the glory of his name;
2. Let all on earth worship and sing praise to you, sing praise to your name!"
3. He has changed the sea in - to dry land; through the river they passed on foot;
4. Hear now, all you who fear God, while I declare what he has done for me.

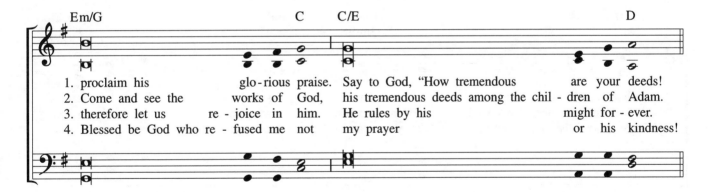

1. proclaim his glo - rious praise. Say to God, "How tremendous are your deeds!
2. Come and see the works of God, his tremendous deeds among the chil - dren of Adam.
3. therefore let us re - joice in him. He rules by his might for - ever.
4. Blessed be God who re - fused me not my prayer or his kindness!

Gospel Acclamation for this celebration may be found on page 234.
A separate assembly response may be found on page 267.

SIXTH SUNDAY OF EASTER — B

Psalm 98: 1, 2–3, 3–4 [56]

Gospel Acclamation for this celebration may be found on page 234.
A separate assembly response may be found on page 273.

SIXTH SUNDAY OF EASTER — C

Psalm 67: 2–3, 5, 6, 8 [57]

RESPONSE: Cantor/All (♩ = ca. 45) [*or:* Alleluia.]

O God, let all the na - tions praise____ you!

VERSES: Cantor or SATB

1. May God have pity on us and bless us; may he let his face shine up - on us.
2. May the nations be glad and ex - ult because you rule the peo - ples in equity;
3. May the peoples praise you, O God; may all the peo - ples praise you!

1. So may your way be known up - on____ earth; among all nations, your sal - vation.
2. [-------------------------------------] the nations on the earth you guide.
3. May God bless____ us, and may all the ends of the earth fear____ him!

Gospel Acclamation for this celebration may be found on page 234.
A separate assembly response may be found on page 271.

ASCENSION OF THE LORD — ABC

Psalm 47: 2–3, 6–7, 8–9 [58]

In several ecclesiastical provinces of the United States of America, the solemnity of the Ascension of the Lord is transferred to the following Sunday. Thursday is observed as an Easter weekday in those archdioceses and dioceses.

Gospel Acclamation for this celebration may be found on page 234.
A separate assembly response may be found on page 264.

SEVENTH SUNDAY OF EASTER — A

Psalm 27: 1, 4, 7–8 [59]

In those places where the observance of the solemnity of the Ascension of the Lord has been transferred to this day, the Mass and readings of the Ascension are used.

RESPONSE: Cantor/All (♩ = *ca. 70*) [*or: Alleluia.*]

I be-lieve that I shall see the good things of the Lord in the land of the liv - ing.

VERSES: Cantor or SATB

1. The LORD is my light and my sal - vation; whom should I fear?
2. One thing I ask of the LORD; this I seek: to dwell in the house of the LORD all the days of my life,
3. Hear, O LORD, the sound of my call; have pity on me, and answer me.

1. The LORD is my life's___ refuge; of whom should I be a - fraid?
2. that I may gaze on the loveliness of the LORD and contem - plate his temple.
3. Of you my heart___ speaks; you my glance___ seeks.

Gospel Acclamation for this celebration may be found on page 234.
A separate assembly response may be found on page 265.

SEVENTH SUNDAY OF EASTER — B

Psalm 103: 1–2, 11–12, 19–20 [60]

In those places where the observance of the solemnity of the Ascension of the Lord has been transferred to this day, the Mass and readings of the Ascension are used.

RESPONSE: Cantor/All (♩ = *ca. 85*) [*or: Alleluia.*]

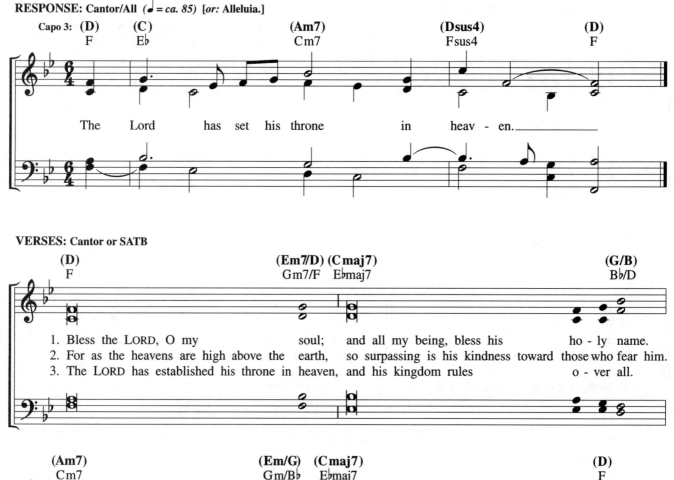

The Lord has set his throne in heav - en.

VERSES: Cantor or SATB

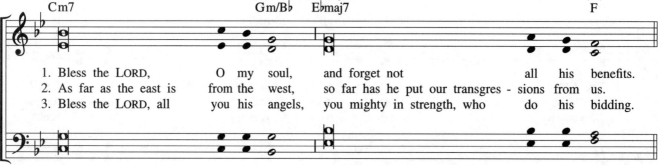

1. Bless the LORD, O my soul; and all my being, bless his ho - ly name.
2. For as the heavens are high above the earth, so surpassing is his kindness toward those who fear him.
3. The LORD has established his throne in heaven, and his kingdom rules o - ver all.

1. Bless the LORD, O my soul, and forget not all his benefits.
2. As far as the east is from the west, so far has he put our transgres - sions from us.
3. Bless the LORD, all you his angels, you mighty in strength, who do his bidding.

Gospel Acclamation for this celebration may be found on page 234.
A separate assembly response may be found on page 273.

SEVENTH SUNDAY OF EASTER — C

Psalm 97: 1–2, 6–7, 9 [61]

In those places where the observance of the solemnity of the Ascension of the Lord has been transferred to this day, the Mass and readings of the Ascension are used.

RESPONSE: Cantor/All (♩ = *ca. 75*) [*or:* Alleluia.]

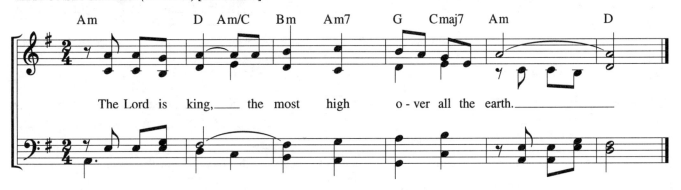

The Lord is king,___ the most high o-ver all the earth.___

VERSES: Cantor or SATB

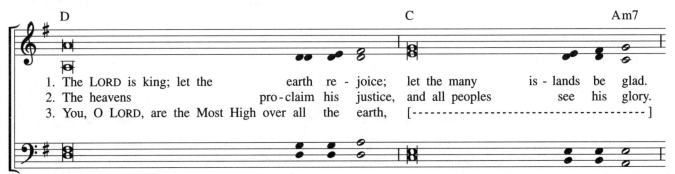

1. The LORD is king; let the earth re-joice; let the many is-lands be glad.
2. The heavens pro-claim his justice, and all peoples see his glory.
3. You, O LORD, are the Most High over all the earth, [--]

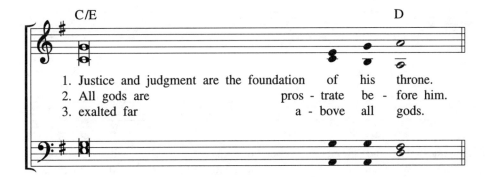

1. Justice and judgment are the foundation of his throne.
2. All gods are pros-trate be-fore him.
3. exalted far a-bove all gods.

Gospel Acclamation for this celebration may be found on page 234.
A separate assembly response may be found on page 274.

Pentecost: Vigil Mass — ABC

Psalm 104: 1–2, 24, 35, 27–28, 29, 30 [62]

RESPONSE (♩. = ca. 40) [*or:* **Alleluia.**]

Descant:
Lord,— send— out, send out— your Spir-it.

Cantor/All:
Lord,— send out your Spir-it, and re-new the face of the earth.

VERSES: Cantor or SATB

1. Bless the LORD, O my soul!	O LORD, my God, you are	great in-deed!
2. How manifold are your works, O LORD!	In wisdom you have	wrought them all—
3. Creatures all look to you	to give them food	in due time.
4. If you take away their breath, they perish	and return	to their dust.

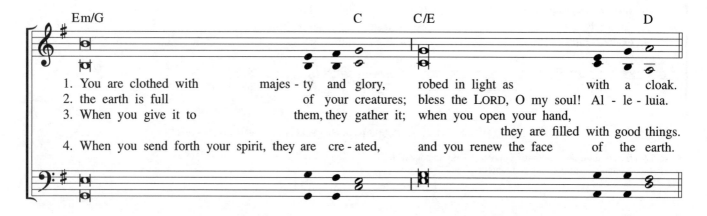

1. You are clothed with majes-ty and glory,	robed in light as	with a cloak.
2. the earth is full of your creatures;	bless the LORD, O my soul!	Al - le - luia.
3. When you give it to them, they gather it;	when you open your hand,	they are filled with good things.
4. When you send forth your spirit, they are cre - ated,	and you renew the face	of the earth.

Gospel Acclamation for this celebration may be found on page 234.
A separate assembly response may be found on page 269.

PENTECOST SUNDAY — ABC

Psalm 104: 1, 24, 29–30, 31, 34 [63]

Gospel Acclamation for this celebration may be found on page 234.
A separate assembly response may be found on page 269.

MOST HOLY TRINITY — A

Daniel 3: 52, 53, 54, 55 [164]

Gospel Acclamation for this celebration may be found on page 235.
A separate assembly response may be found on page 264.

MOST HOLY TRINITY — B

Psalm 33: 4–5, 6, 9, 18–19, 20, 22 [165]

RESPONSE (♩ = ca. 85)

Descant

Bless'd___ the peo - ple, to be his own.

Cantor/All

Bless'd___ the peo - ple___ the Lord has cho - sen to be his own.___

VERSES: Cantor or SATB

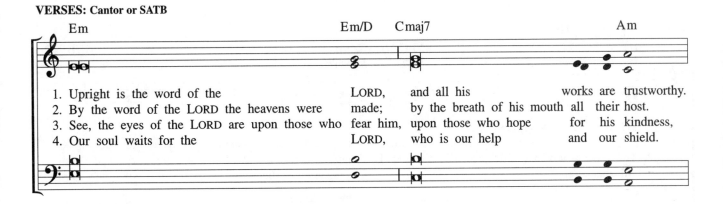

1. Upright is the word of the LORD, and all his works are trustworthy.
2. By the word of the LORD the heavens were made; by the breath of his mouth all their host.
3. See, the eyes of the LORD are upon those who fear him, upon those who hope for his kindness,
4. Our soul waits for the LORD, who is our help and our shield.

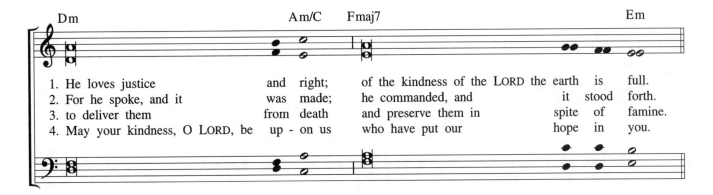

1. He loves justice and right; of the kindness of the LORD the earth is full.
2. For he spoke, and it was made; he commanded, and it stood forth.
3. to deliver them from death and preserve them in spite of famine.
4. May your kindness, O LORD, be up - on us who have put our hope in you.

Gospel Acclamation for this celebration may be found on page 235.
A separate assembly response may be found on page 263.

MOST HOLY TRINITY — C

Psalm 8: 4–5, 6–7, 8–9 [166]

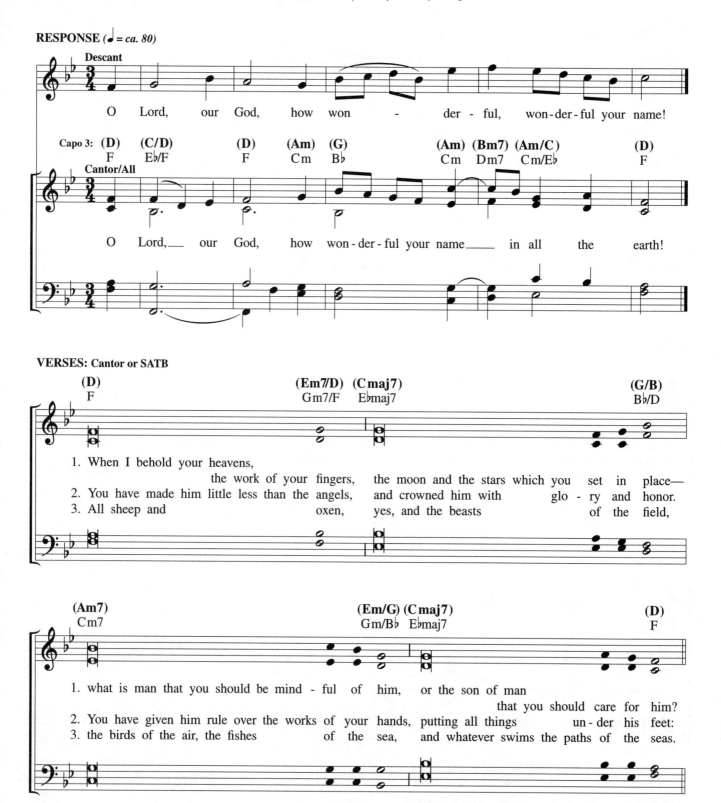

Gospel Acclamation for this celebration may be found on page 235.
A separate assembly response may be found on page 271.

MOST HOLY BODY AND BLOOD OF CHRIST — A

Psalm 147: 12–13, 14–15, 19–20 [167]

Gospel Acclamation for this celebration may be found on page 235.
A separate assembly response may be found on page 271.

MOST HOLY BODY AND BLOOD OF CHRIST — B

Psalm 116: 12–13, 15–16, 17–18 [168]

Gospel Acclamation for this celebration may be found on page 235.
A separate assembly response may be found on page 266.

MOST HOLY BODY AND BLOOD OF CHRIST — C

Psalm 110: 1, 2, 3, 4 [169]

Gospel Acclamation for this celebration may be found on page 235.
A separate assembly response may be found on page 277.

MOST SACRED HEART OF JESUS — A

Psalm 103: 1–2, 3–4, 6–7, 8, 10 [170]

Gospel Acclamation for this celebration may be found on page 235.
A separate assembly response may be found on page 275.

MOST SACRED HEART OF JESUS — B

Isaiah 12: 2–3, 4, 5–6 [171]

RESPONSE: Cantor/All (♩ = *ca. 105*)

You will draw wa - ter___ joy - ful - ly___ from the springs of sal - va - tion.___

VERSES: Cantor or SATB

1a. God indeed is my savior; I am confident and un - a - fraid. **(to 1b)**
1b. My strength and my courage is the LORD, and he has been my savior. **(to 1c)**
 2. Give thanks to the LORD, ac - claim his name; among the nations make known his deeds,
 3. Sing praise to the LORD for his glo - rious a - chievement; let this be known throughout all the earth.

1c. With joy you will draw water at the fountain of sal - vation.
 2. [--] proclaim how exalted is his name.
 3. Shout with exultation, O cit - y of Zion, for great in your midst is the Holy One of Israel!

Gospel Acclamation for this celebration may be found on page 235.
A separate assembly response may be found on page 277.

MOST SACRED HEART OF JESUS — C

Psalm 23: 1–3a, 3b–4, 5, 6 [172]

RESPONSE: Cantor/All (♩. = *ca. 40*)

The Lord_____ is my shep-herd; there is noth-ing I shall want._____

VERSES: Cantor or SATB

1. The LORD is my shepherd; I shall not want. In verdant pastures he gives me re-pose;
2. He guides me in right paths for his name's sake. Even though I walk in the dark valley I fear no evil;
3. You spread the table be-fore me in the sight of my foes;
4. Only goodness and kindness follow me all the days of my life;

1. beside restful wa-ters he leads me; he refreshes my soul.
2. for you are at my side with your rod and your staff that give me courage.
3. you anoint my head with oil; my cup over-flows.
4. and I shall dwell in the house of the LORD for years to come.

Gospel Acclamation for this celebration may be found on page 235.
A separate assembly response may be found on page 274.

SECOND SUNDAY IN ORDINARY TIME — A

Psalm 40: 2, 4, 7–8, 8–9, 10 [64]

RESPONSE: Cantor/All (♩ = *ca. 90*)

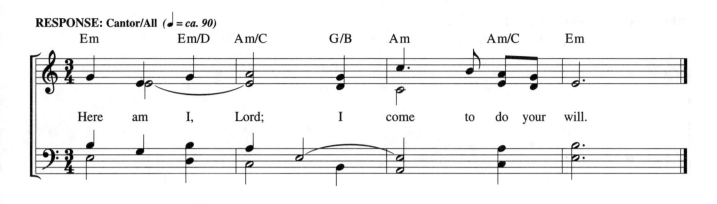

Here am I, Lord; I come to do your will.

VERSES: Cantor or SATB

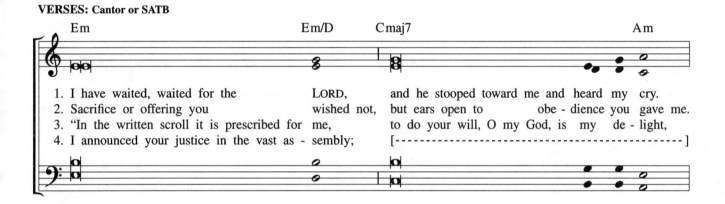

1. I have waited, waited for the LORD, and he stooped toward me and heard my cry.
2. Sacrifice or offering you wished not, but ears open to obe - dience you gave me.
3. "In the written scroll it is prescribed for me, to do your will, O my God, is my de - light,
4. I announced your justice in the vast as - sembly; [--]

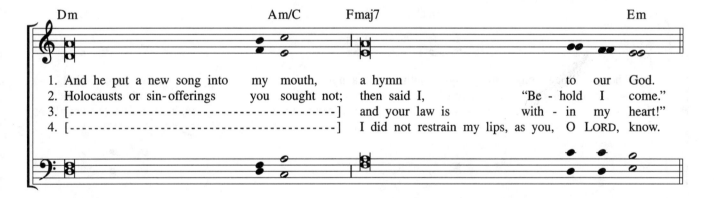

1. And he put a new song into my mouth, a hymn to our God.
2. Holocausts or sin-offerings you sought not; then said I, "Be - hold I come."
3. [--] and your law is with - in my heart!"
4. [--] I did not restrain my lips, as you, O LORD, know.

Gospel Acclamation for this celebration may be found on page 236.
A separate assembly response may be found on page 265.

SECOND SUNDAY IN ORDINARY TIME — B

Psalm 40: 2, 4, 7–8, 8–9, 10 [65]

RESPONSE: Cantor/All (♩ = ca. 90)

Here am I, Lord; I come to do your will.

VERSES: Cantor or SATB

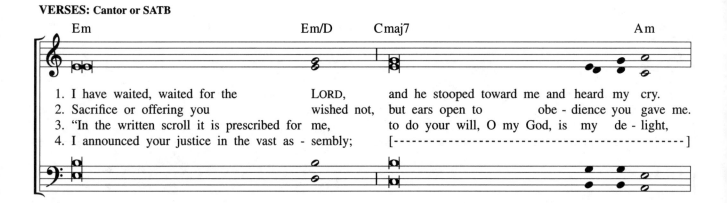

1. I have waited, waited for the LORD, and he stooped toward me and heard my cry.
2. Sacrifice or offering you wished not, but ears open to obe - dience you gave me.
3. "In the written scroll it is prescribed for me, to do your will, O my God, is my de - light,
4. I announced your justice in the vast as - sembly; [--]

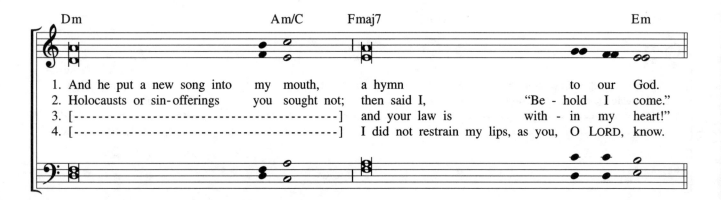

1. And he put a new song into my mouth, a hymn to our God.
2. Holocausts or sin-offerings you sought not; then said I, "Be - hold I come."
3. [---] and your law is with - in my heart!"
4. [---] I did not restrain my lips, as you, O LORD, know.

Gospel Acclamation for this celebration may be found on page 242.
A separate assembly response may be found on page 265.

SECOND SUNDAY IN ORDINARY TIME — C

Psalm 96: 1–2, 2–3, 7–8, 9–10 [66]

RESPONSE: Cantor/All (♩ = *ca. 110*)

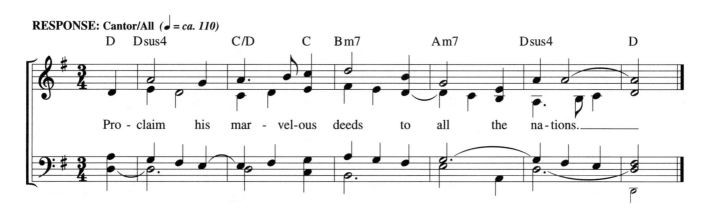

Pro - claim his mar - vel-ous deeds to all the na-tions.

VERSES: Cantor or SATB

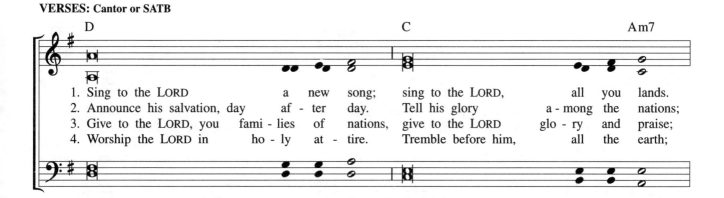

1. Sing to the LORD a new song; sing to the LORD, all you lands.
2. Announce his salvation, day af - ter day. Tell his glory a - mong the nations;
3. Give to the LORD, you fami - lies of nations, give to the LORD glo - ry and praise;
4. Worship the LORD in ho - ly at - tire. Tremble before him, all the earth;

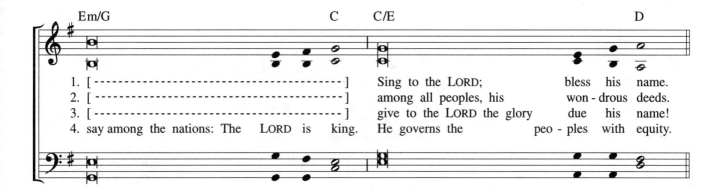

1. [---] Sing to the LORD; bless his name.
2. [---] among all peoples, his won - drous deeds.
3. [---] give to the LORD the glory due his name!
4. say among the nations: The LORD is king. He governs the peo - ples with equity.

Gospel Acclamation for this celebration may be found on page 248.
A separate assembly response may be found on page 272.

THIRD SUNDAY IN ORDINARY TIME — A

Psalm 27: 1, 4, 13–14 [67]

Gospel Acclamation for this celebration may be found on page 236.
A separate assembly response may be found on page 274.

THIRD SUNDAY IN ORDINARY TIME — B

Psalm 25: 4–5, 6–7, 8–9 [68]

Gospel Acclamation for this celebration may be found on page 242.
A separate assembly response may be found on page 273.

THIRD SUNDAY IN ORDINARY TIME — C

Psalm 19: 8, 9, 10, 15 [69]

Gospel Acclamation for this celebration may be found on page 248.
A separate assembly response may be found on page 278.

FOURTH SUNDAY IN ORDINARY TIME — A

Psalm 146: 6–7, 8–9, 9–10 [70]

RESPONSE: Cantor/All (♩ = *ca. 70*) [*or:* Alleluia.]

Bless'd are the poor in spir-it;___ the king-dom of heav'n is theirs!

VERSES: Cantor or SATB

1. The LORD keeps faith for-ever, secures justice for the op-pressed,
2. The LORD gives sight to the blind; the LORD raises up those who were bowed down.
3. The fatherless and the widow the LORD sus-tains, but the way of the wick-ed he thwarts.

1. gives food to the hungry. The LORD sets cap-tives free.
2. The LORD loves the just; the LORD pro-tects strangers.
3. The LORD shall reign for-ever; your God, O Zion, through all generations. Al-le-luia.

Gospel Acclamation for this celebration may be found on page 236.
A separate assembly response may be found on page 262.

FOURTH SUNDAY IN ORDINARY TIME — B

Psalm 95: 1–2, 6–7, 7–9 [71]

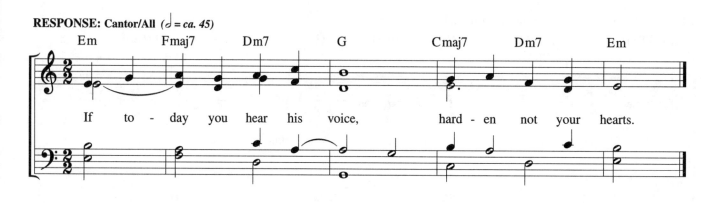

RESPONSE: Cantor/All (♩ = ca. 45)

If to-day you hear his voice, hard-en not your hearts.

VERSES: Cantor or SATB

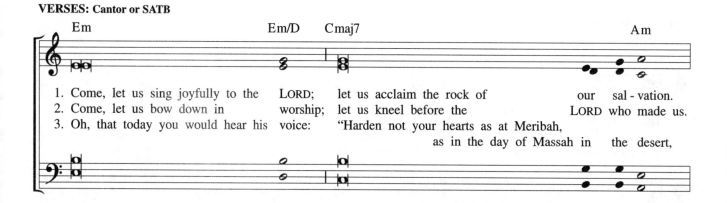

1. Come, let us sing joyfully to the LORD; let us acclaim the rock of our sal-vation.
2. Come, let us bow down in worship; let us kneel before the LORD who made us.
3. Oh, that today you would hear his voice: "Harden not your hearts as at Meribah, as in the day of Massah in the desert,

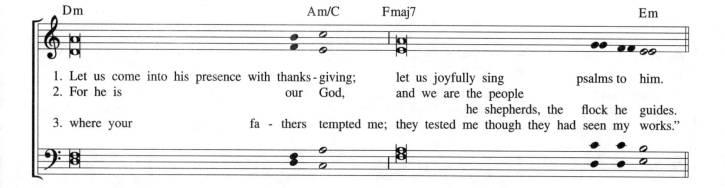

1. Let us come into his presence with thanks-giving; let us joyfully sing psalms to him.
2. For he is our God, and we are the people he shepherds, the flock he guides.
3. where your fa-thers tempted me; they tested me though they had seen my works."

Gospel Acclamation for this celebration may be found on page 242.
A separate assembly response may be found on page 266.

FOURTH SUNDAY IN ORDINARY TIME — C

Psalm 71: 1–2, 3–4, 5–6, 15, 17 [72]

RESPONSE: Cantor/All (♩ = ca. 85)

I will sing of your sal - va - tion, sing___ of your sal - va - tion.___

VERSES: Cantor or SATB

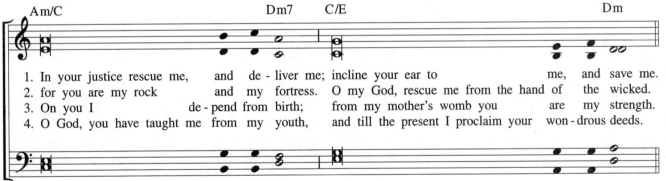

1. In you, O LORD, I take refuge; let me never be put to shame.
2. Be my rock of refuge, a stonghold to give me safety,
3. For you are my hope, O Lord; my trust, O God, from my youth.
4. My mouth shall de - clare your justice, day by day your sal - vation.

1. In your justice rescue me, and de - liver me; incline your ear to me, and save me.
2. for you are my rock and my fortress. O my God, rescue me from the hand of the wicked.
3. On you I de - pend from birth; from my mother's womb you are my strength.
4. O God, you have taught me from my youth, and till the present I proclaim your won - drous deeds.

Gospel Acclamation for this celebration may be found on page 248.
A separate assembly response may be found on page 266.

FIFTH SUNDAY IN ORDINARY TIME — A

Psalm 112: 4–5, 6–7, 8–9 [73]

RESPONSE: Cantor/All (♩ = ca. 40) [or: Alleluia.]

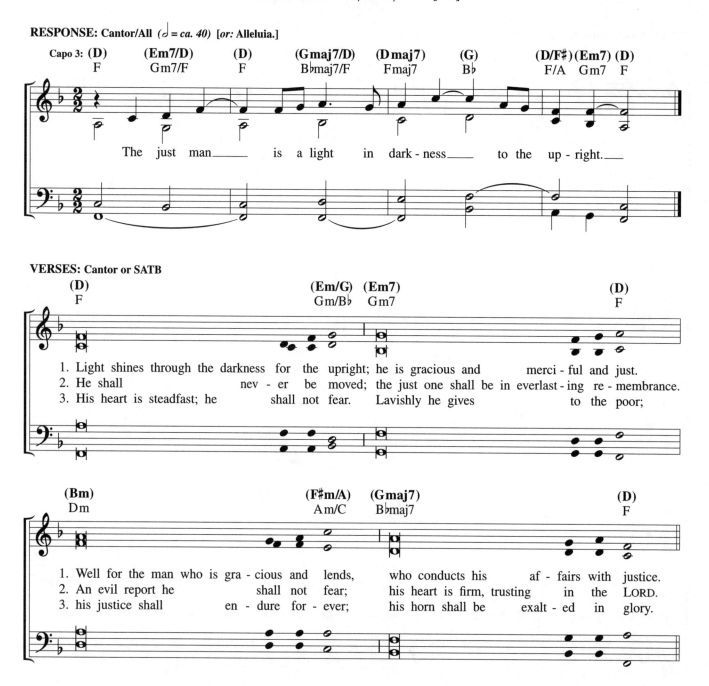

The just man is a light in dark-ness to the up-right.

VERSES: Cantor or SATB

1. Light shines through the darkness for the upright; he is gracious and merci-ful and just.
2. He shall nev-er be moved; the just one shall be in everlast-ing re-membrance.
3. His heart is steadfast; he shall not fear. Lavishly he gives to the poor;

1. Well for the man who is gra-cious and lends, who conducts his af-fairs with justice.
2. An evil report he shall not fear; his heart is firm, trusting in the LORD.
3. his justice shall en-dure for-ever; his horn shall be exalt-ed in glory.

Gospel Acclamation for this celebration may be found on page 236.
A separate assembly response may be found on page 273.

FIFTH SUNDAY IN ORDINARY TIME — B

Psalm 147: 1–2, 3–4, 5–6 [74]

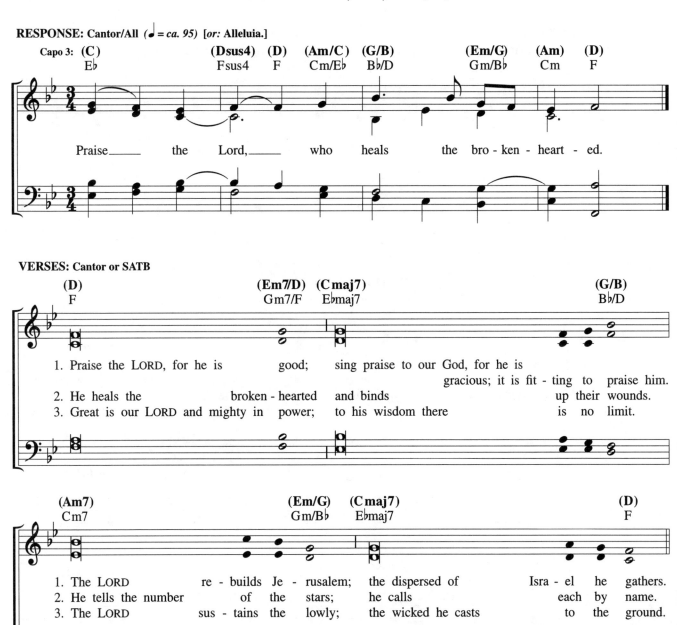

RESPONSE: Cantor/All (♩ = ca. 95) [or: Alleluia.]

Praise the Lord, who heals the bro-ken-heart-ed.

VERSES: Cantor or SATB

1. Praise the LORD, for he is good; sing praise to our God, for he is gracious; it is fit-ting to praise him.
2. He heals the broken-hearted and binds up their wounds.
3. Great is our LORD and mighty in power; to his wisdom there is no limit.

1. The LORD re-builds Je-rusalem; the dispersed of Isra-el he gathers.
2. He tells the number of the stars; he calls each by name.
3. The LORD sus-tains the lowly; the wicked he casts to the ground.

Gospel Acclamation for this celebration may be found on page 242.
A separate assembly response may be found on page 272.

FIFTH SUNDAY IN ORDINARY TIME — C

Psalm 138: 1–2, 2–3, 4–5, 7–8 [75]

RESPONSE: Cantor/All (♩ = *ca. 75*)

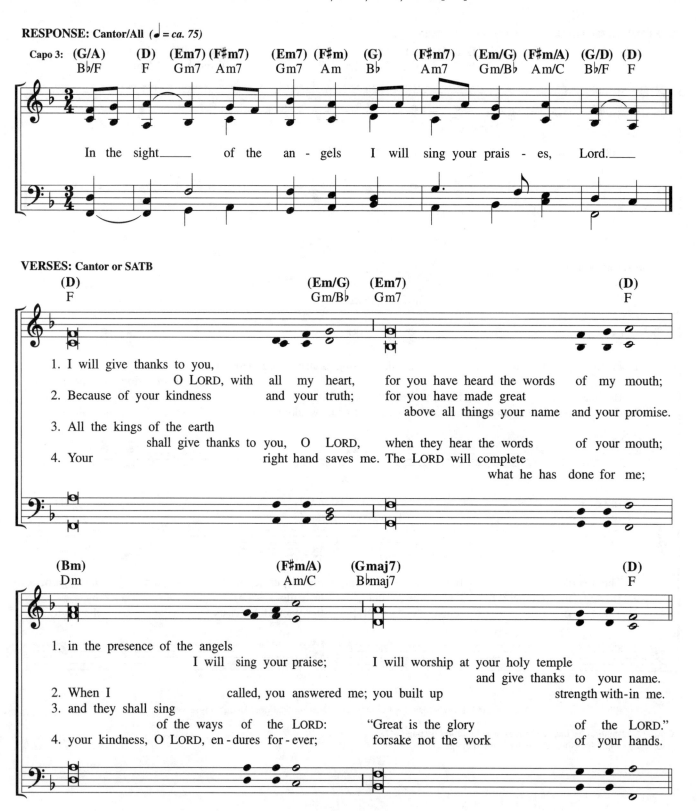

In the sight___ of the an-gels I will sing your prais - es, Lord.___

VERSES: Cantor or SATB

1. I will give thanks to you,
   O LORD, with all my heart, for you have heard the words of my mouth;
2. Because of your kindness and your truth; for you have made great
   above all things your name and your promise.
3. All the kings of the earth
   shall give thanks to you, O LORD, when they hear the words of your mouth;
4. Your right hand saves me. The LORD will complete
   what he has done for me;

1. in the presence of the angels
   I will sing your praise; I will worship at your holy temple
   and give thanks to your name.
2. When I called, you answered me; you built up strength with-in me.
3. and they shall sing
   of the ways of the LORD: "Great is the glory of the LORD."
4. your kindness, O LORD, en-dures for-ever; forsake not the work of your hands.

Gospel Acclamation for this celebration may be found on page 248.
A separate assembly response may be found on page 267.

Sixth Sunday in Ordinary Time — A

Psalm 119: 1–2, 4–5, 17–18, 33–34 [76]

Gospel Acclamation for this celebration may be found on page 236.
A separate assembly response may be found on page 262.

SIXTH SUNDAY IN ORDINARY TIME — B

Psalm 32: 1–2, 5, 11 [77]

RESPONSE: Cantor/All (♩. = ca. 50)

I turn to you, Lord, in time of trou-ble, and you fill me with the joy of sal - va - tion.___

VERSES: Cantor or SATB

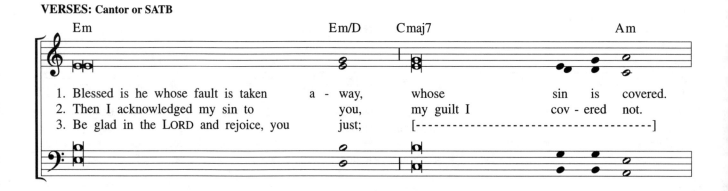

1. Blessed is he whose fault is taken a - way, whose sin is covered.
2. Then I acknowledged my sin to you, my guilt I cov - ered not.
3. Be glad in the LORD and rejoice, you just; [---------------------------------------]

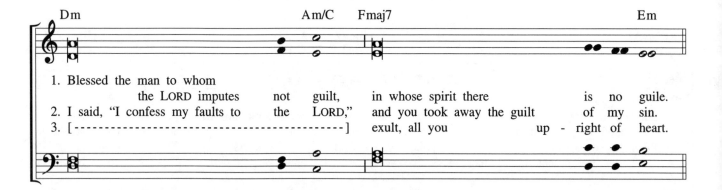

1. Blessed the man to whom the LORD imputes not guilt, in whose spirit there is no guile.
2. I said, "I confess my faults to the LORD," and you took away the guilt of my sin.
3. [---------------------------------------] exult, all you up - right of heart.

Gospel Acclamation for this celebration may be found on page 242.
A separate assembly response may be found on page 265.

SIXTH SUNDAY IN ORDINARY TIME — C

Psalm 1: 1–2, 3, 4 and 6 [78]

RESPONSE: Cantor/All (♩ = ca. 60)

Bless'd_____ are they_____ who hope in the Lord.

VERSES: Cantor or SATB

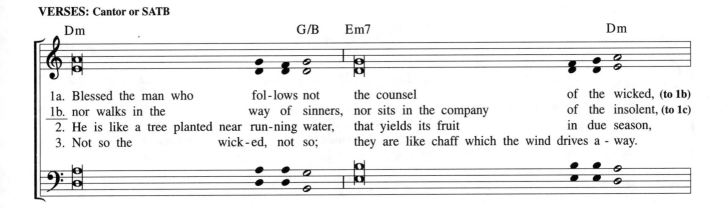

1a. Blessed the man who fol-lows not the counsel of the wicked, **(to 1b)**
1b. nor walks in the way of sinners, nor sits in the company of the insolent, **(to 1c)**
2. He is like a tree planted near run-ning water, that yields its fruit in due season,
3. Not so the wick-ed, not so; they are like chaff which the wind drives a - way.

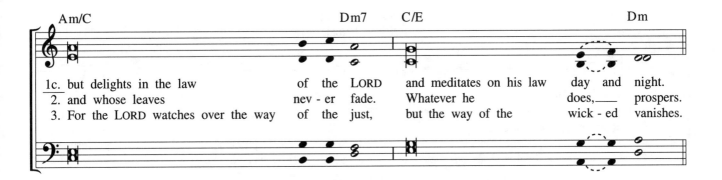

1c. but delights in the law of the LORD and meditates on his law day and night.
2. and whose leaves nev - er fade. Whatever he does,___ prospers.
3. For the LORD watches over the way of the just, but the way of the wick - ed vanishes.

Gospel Acclamation for this celebration may be found on page 248.
A separate assembly response may be found on page 262.

SEVENTH SUNDAY IN ORDINARY TIME — A

Psalm 103: 1–2, 3–4, 8, 10, 12–13 [79]

Gospel Acclamation for this celebration may be found on page 236.
A separate assembly response may be found on page 274.

SEVENTH SUNDAY IN ORDINARY TIME — B

Psalm 41: 2–3, 4–5, 13–14 [80]

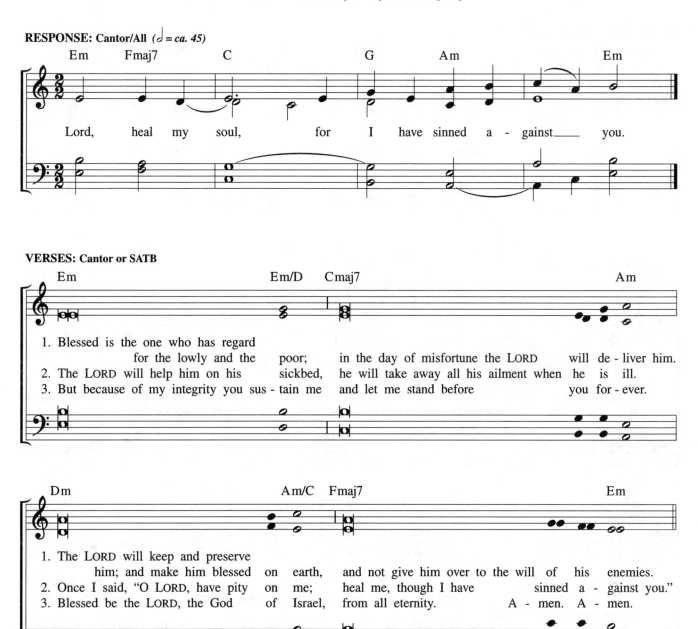

RESPONSE: Cantor/All (♩ = ca. 45)

Lord, heal my soul, for I have sinned a - gainst____ you.

VERSES: Cantor or SATB

1. Blessed is the one who has regard for the lowly and the poor; in the day of misfortune the LORD will de - liver him.
2. The LORD will help him on his sickbed, he will take away all his ailment when he is ill.
3. But because of my integrity you sus - tain me and let me stand before you for - ever.

1. The LORD will keep and preserve him; and make him blessed on earth, and not give him over to the will of his enemies.
2. Once I said, "O LORD, have pity on me; heal me, though I have sinned a - gainst you."
3. Blessed be the LORD, the God of Israel, from all eternity. A - men. A - men.

Gospel Acclamation for this celebration may be found on page 242.
A separate assembly response may be found on page 268.

SEVENTH SUNDAY IN ORDINARY TIME — C

Psalm 103: 1–2, 3–4, 8, 10, 12–13 [81]

RESPONSE: Cantor/All (♩ = ca. 100)

The Lord is kind and mer-ci-ful, kind and mer-ci-ful.

VERSES: Cantor or SATB

1. Bless the LORD, O my soul; and all my being, bless his ho-ly name.
2. He pardons all your in-iquities, heals all your ills.
3. Merciful and gracious is the LORD, slow to anger and abound-ing in kindness.
4. As far as the east is from the west, so far has he put our transgres-sions from us.

1. Bless the LORD, O my soul, and forget not all his benefits.
2. He redeems your life from de-struction, crowns you with kindness and com-passion.
3. Not according to our sins does he deal with us, nor does he requite us according to our crimes.
4. As a father has compassion on his children, so the LORD has compassion on those who fear him.

Gospel Acclamation for this celebration may be found on page 248.
A separate assembly response may be found on page 274.

EIGHTH SUNDAY IN ORDINARY TIME — A

Psalm 62: 2–3, 6–7, 8–9 [82]

RESPONSE: Cantor/All (♩ = ca. 80)

Rest in God a - lone, _____ my soul. _____

VERSES: Cantor or SATB

1. Only in God is my soul at rest; from him comes my sal - vation.
2. Only in God be at rest, my soul, for from him comes my hope.
3. With God is my safety and my glory, he is the rock of my strength; my refuge is in God.

1. He only is my rock and my sal - vation, my stronghold; I shall not be dis - turbed at all.
2. He only is my rock and my sal - vation, my stronghold; I shall not be dis - turbed.
3. Trust in him at all times, O my people! Pour out your hearts be - fore him.

Gospel Acclamation for this celebration may be found on page 237.
A separate assembly response may be found on page 272.

EIGHTH SUNDAY IN ORDINARY TIME — B

Psalm 103: 1–2, 3–4, 8, 10, 12–13 [83]

RESPONSE: Cantor/All (♩ = ca. 100)

The Lord is kind and mer-ci-ful, kind and mer-ci-ful.

VERSES: Cantor or SATB

1. Bless the LORD, O my soul; and all my being, bless his ho-ly name.
2. He pardons all your in-iquities, heals all your ills.
3. Merciful and gracious is the LORD, slow to anger and abound-ing in kindness.
4. As far as the east is from the west, so far has he put our transgres-sions from us.

1. Bless the LORD, O my soul, and forget not all his benefits.
2. He redeems your life from de-struction, crowns you with kindness and com-passion.
3. Not according to our sins does he deal with us, nor does he requite us according to our crimes.
4. As a father has compassion on his children, so the Lord has compassion on those who fear him.

Gospel Acclamation for this celebration may be found on page 243.
A separate assembly response may be found on page 274.

EIGHTH SUNDAY IN ORDINARY TIME — C

Psalm 92: 2–3, 13–14, 15–16 [84]

RESPONSE: Cantor/All (♩ = ca. 85)

Lord, it is good to give thanks to you.

VERSES: Cantor or SATB

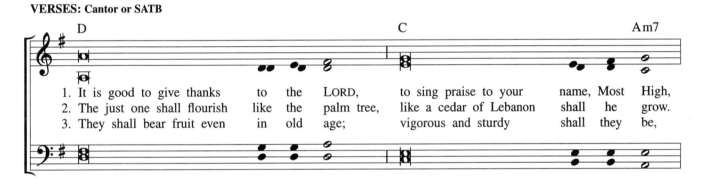

1. It is good to give thanks to the LORD, to sing praise to your name, Most High,
2. The just one shall flourish like the palm tree, like a cedar of Lebanon shall he grow.
3. They shall bear fruit even in old age; vigorous and sturdy shall they be,

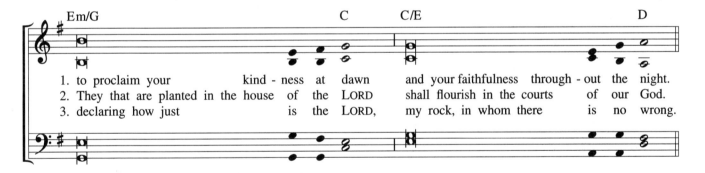

1. to proclaim your kind-ness at dawn and your faithfulness through-out the night.
2. They that are planted in the house of the LORD shall flourish in the courts of our God.
3. declaring how just is the LORD, my rock, in whom there is no wrong.

Gospel Acclamation for this celebration may be found on page 249.
A separate assembly response may be found on page 269.

NINTH SUNDAY IN ORDINARY TIME — A

Psalm 31: 2–3, 3–4, 17, 25 [85]

RESPONSE: Cantor/All (♩ = ca. 80)

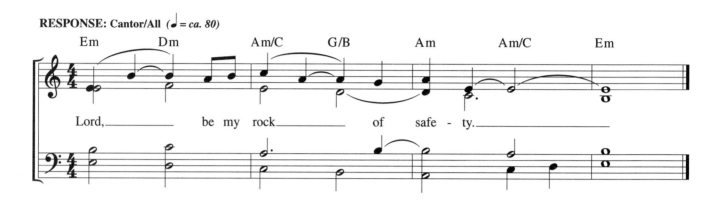

Lord, be my rock of safe-ty.

VERSES: Cantor or SATB

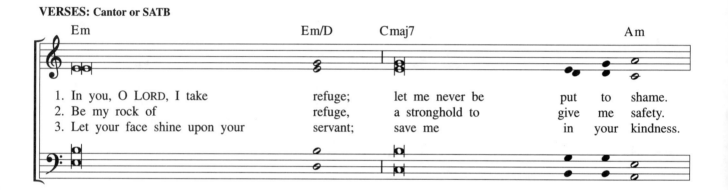

1. In you, O LORD, I take refuge; let me never be put to shame.
2. Be my rock of refuge, a stronghold to give me safety.
3. Let your face shine upon your servant; save me in your kindness.

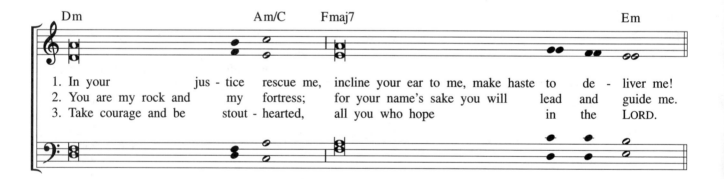

1. In your jus-tice rescue me, incline your ear to me, make haste to de-liver me!
2. You are my rock and my fortress; for your name's sake you will lead and guide me.
3. Take courage and be stout-hearted, all you who hope in the LORD.

Gospel Acclamation for this celebration may be found on page 237.
A separate assembly response may be found on page 268.

NINTH SUNDAY IN ORDINARY TIME — B

Psalm 81: 3–4, 5–6, 6–8, 10–11 [86]

RESPONSE: Cantor/All (♩ = ca. 70)

Sing_____ with joy_____ to God our help.

VERSES: Cantor or SATB

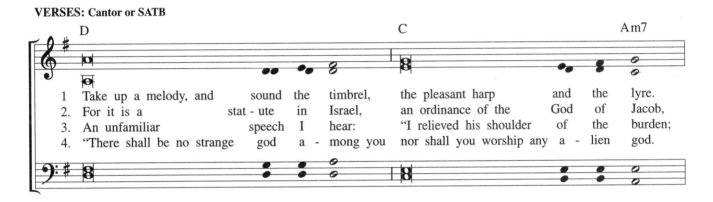

1. Take up a melody, and sound the timbrel, the pleasant harp and the lyre.
2. For it is a stat-ute in Israel, an ordinance of the God of Jacob,
3. An unfamiliar speech I hear: "I relieved his shoulder of the burden;
4. "There shall be no strange god a-mong you nor shall you worship any a-lien god.

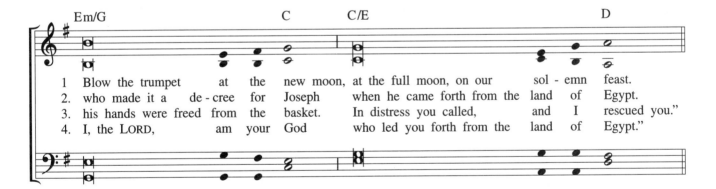

1. Blow the trumpet at the new moon, at the full moon, on our sol-emn feast.
2. who made it a de-cree for Joseph when he came forth from the land of Egypt.
3. his hands were freed from the basket. In distress you called, and I rescued you."
4. I, the LORD, am your God who led you forth from the land of Egypt."

Gospel Acclamation for this celebration may be found on page 243.
A separate assembly response may be found on page 272.

NINTH SUNDAY IN ORDINARY TIME — C

Psalm 117: 1, 2 [87]

RESPONSE: Cantor/All (♩ = *ca. 110*) [*or: Alleluia.*]

Go out to all the world and tell the Good News.

VERSES: Cantor or SATB

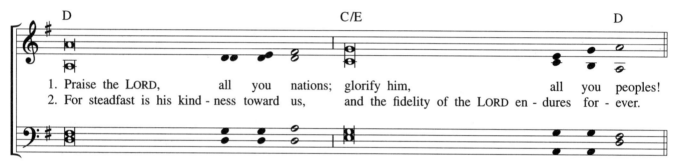

1. Praise the LORD, all you nations; glorify him, all you peoples!
2. For steadfast is his kind - ness toward us, and the fidelity of the LORD en - dures for - ever.

Gospel Acclamation for this celebration may be found on page 249.
A separate assembly response may be found on page 264.

10TH SUNDAY IN ORDINARY TIME — A

Psalm 50: 1, 8, 12–13, 14–15 [88]

RESPONSE: Cantor/All (♩ = ca. 75)

VERSES: Cantor or SATB

To the up-right I will show the sav-ing pow'r of God.

1. God the LORD has spoken and sum-moned the earth, from the rising of the sun to its setting.
2. "If I were hungry, I would not tell you, for mine are the world and its fullness.
3. "Offer to God praise as your sacrifice and fulfill your vows to the Most High;

1. "Not for your sacrifices do I re-buke you, for your holocausts are be-fore me always."
2. Do I eat the flesh of strong bulls, or is the blood of goats my drink?"
3. then call upon me in time of dis-tress; I will rescue you, and you shall glo-ri-fy me."

Gospel Acclamation for this celebration may be found on page 237.
A separate assembly response may be found on page 276.

10TH SUNDAY IN ORDINARY TIME — B

Psalm 130: 1–2, 3–4, 5–6, 7–8 [89]

RESPONSE: Cantor/All (♩ = ca. 55)

With the Lord there is mer-cy,_____ and full-ness of re-demp-tion, full-ness of re-demp-tion._____

VERSES: Cantor or SATB

1. Out of the depths I cry to you, O LORD; LORD, hear my voice!
2. If you, O LORD, mark in-iquities, LORD, who can stand?
3. I trust in the LORD; my soul trusts in his word.
4. For with the LORD is kindness and with him is plen-teous re-demption;

1. Let your ears be at-tentive to my voice in sup-pli-cation.
2. But with you is for-giveness, that you may be re-vered.
3. More than sentinels wait for the dawn, let Israel wait for the LORD.
4. and he will re-deem Israel from all their in-iquities.

Gospel Acclamation for this celebration may be found on page 243.
A separate assembly response may be found on page 277.

10th Sunday in Ordinary Time — C

Psalm 30: 2, 4, 5–6, 11, 12, 13 [90]

RESPONSE: Cantor/All (♩ = *ca. 75*)

I will praise_____ you, Lord, for you have res - cued me._____

VERSES: Cantor or SATB

1. I will extol you, O LORD, for you drew me clear   and did not let my
                                                         enemies rejoice o - ver me.
2a. Sing praise to the LORD, you his   faith-ful ones,   and give thanks to his   ho - ly   name. **(to 2b)**
2b. For his anger lasts   but   a   moment; a lifetime,   his good will.   **(to 2c)**
3. Hear, O LORD, and have   pit - y   on me;   O LORD,   be   my   helper.

1. O LORD, you brought me up from the nether world; you preserved me from among
                                                         those going down in - to   the pit.
2c. At nightfall, weeping   en - ters in,   but with the   dawn, re - joicing.
3. You changed my mourning   in - to dancing;   O LORD, my God, forever will I   give you thanks.

Gospel Acclamation for this celebration may be found on page 249.
A separate assembly response may be found on page 266.

11TH SUNDAY IN ORDINARY TIME — A

Psalm 100: 1–2, 3, 5 [91]

Gospel Acclamation for this celebration may be found on page 237.
A separate assembly response may be found on page 277.

11TH SUNDAY IN ORDINARY TIME — B

Psalm 92: 2–3, 13–14, 15–16 [92]

RESPONSE: Cantor/All (♩ = *ca. 85*)

Lord, _____ it is good to give thanks _____ to you.

VERSES: Cantor or SATB

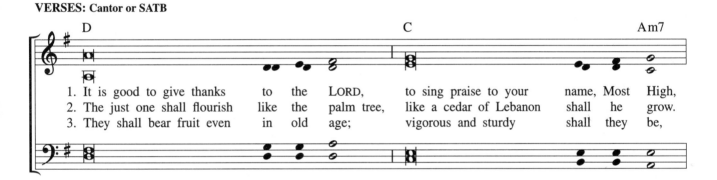

1. It is good to give thanks to the LORD, to sing praise to your name, Most High,
2. The just one shall flourish like the palm tree, like a cedar of Lebanon shall he grow.
3. They shall bear fruit even in old age; vigorous and sturdy shall they be,

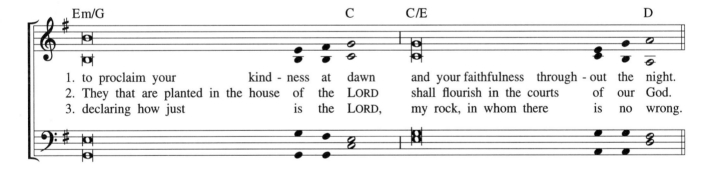

1. to proclaim your kind-ness at dawn and your faithfulness through-out the night.
2. They that are planted in the house of the LORD shall flourish in the courts of our God.
3. declaring how just is the LORD, my rock, in whom there is no wrong.

Gospel Acclamation for this celebration may be found on page 243.
A separate assembly response may be found on page 269.

11TH SUNDAY IN ORDINARY TIME — C

Psalm 32: 1–2, 5, 7, 11 [93]

RESPONSE: Cantor/All (♩ = *ca. 70*)

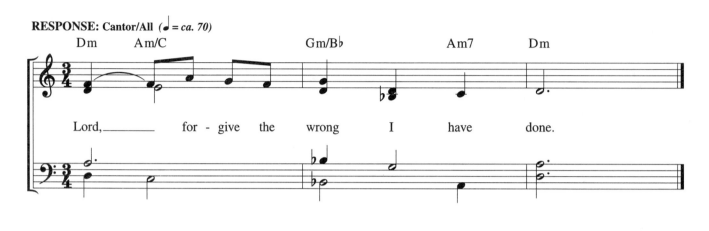

Lord,_____ for-give the wrong I have done.

VERSES: Cantor or SATB

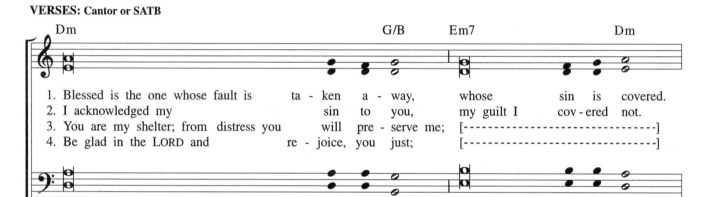

1. Blessed is the one whose fault is ta - ken a - way, whose sin is covered.
2. I acknowledged my sin to you, my guilt I cov - ered not.
3. You are my shelter; from distress you will pre - serve me; [-------------------------------]
4. Be glad in the LORD and re - joice, you just; [-------------------------------]

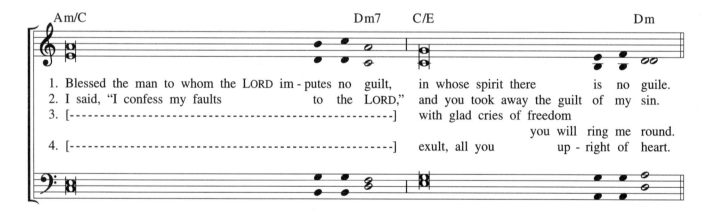

1. Blessed the man to whom the LORD im - putes no guilt, in whose spirit there is no guile.
2. I said, "I confess my faults to the LORD," and you took away the guilt of my sin.
3. [--] with glad cries of freedom you will ring me round.
4. [--] exult, all you up - right of heart.

Gospel Acclamation for this celebration may be found on page 249.
A separate assembly response may be found on page 268.

12th Sunday in Ordinary Time — A

Psalm 69: 8–10, 14, 17, 33–35 [94]

RESPONSE: Cantor/All (♩. = ca. 40)

Lord, in your great love, an-swer me, an-swer me.

VERSES: Cantor or SATB

1. For your sake I bear insult, and shame cov-ers my face.
2. I pray to you, O LORD, for the time of your fa-vor, O God!
3. "See, you lowly ones, and be glad; you who seek God, may your hearts re-vive!

1. I have become an outcast to my brothers, a stranger to my moth-er's children,
2. In your great kind-ness answer me with your con-stant help.
3. For the LORD hears the poor, and his own who are in bonds he spurns not.

1. because zeal for your house con-sumes me, and the insults of those who blaspheme you fall up-on me.
2. Answer me, O LORD, for bounteous is your kindness; in your great mercy turn toward me.
3. Let the heavens and the earth praise him, the seas and whatever moves in them!"

Gospel Acclamation for this celebration may be found on page 237.
A separate assembly response may be found on page 269.

12TH SUNDAY IN ORDINARY TIME — B

Psalm 107: 23–24, 25–26, 28–29, 30–31 [95]

Gospel Acclamation for this celebration may be found on page 243.
A separate assembly response may be found on page 264.

12TH SUNDAY IN ORDINARY TIME — C

Psalm 63: 2, 3–4, 5–6, 8–9 [96]

RESPONSE: Cantor/All (♩ = *ca. 42*)

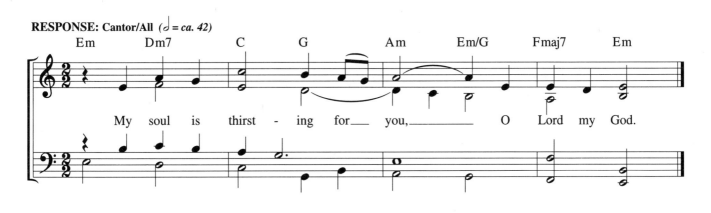

My soul is thirst-ing for you, O Lord my God.

VERSES: Cantor or SATB

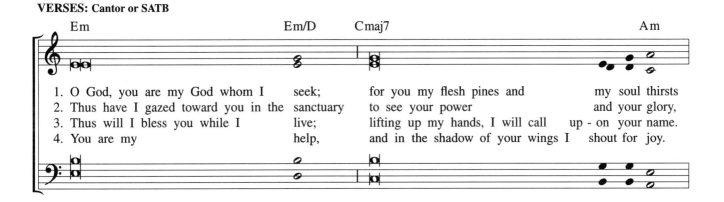

1. O God, you are my God whom I seek; for you my flesh pines and my soul thirsts
2. Thus have I gazed toward you in the sanctuary to see your power and your glory,
3. Thus will I bless you while I live; lifting up my hands, I will call up-on your name.
4. You are my help, and in the shadow of your wings I shout for joy.

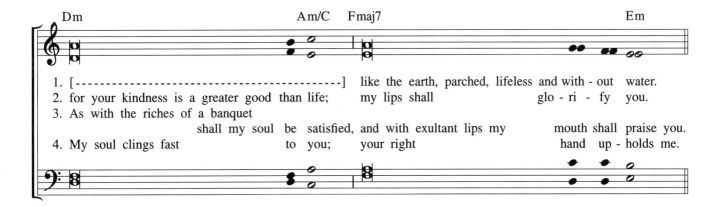

1. [--] like the earth, parched, lifeless and with-out water.
2. for your kindness is a greater good than life; my lips shall glo-ri-fy you.
3. As with the riches of a banquet shall my soul be satisfied, and with exultant lips my mouth shall praise you.
4. My soul clings fast to you; your right hand up-holds me.

Gospel Acclamation for this celebration may be found on page 249.
A separate assembly response may be found on page 270.

13TH SUNDAY IN ORDINARY TIME — A

Psalm 89: 2–3, 16–17, 18–19 [97]

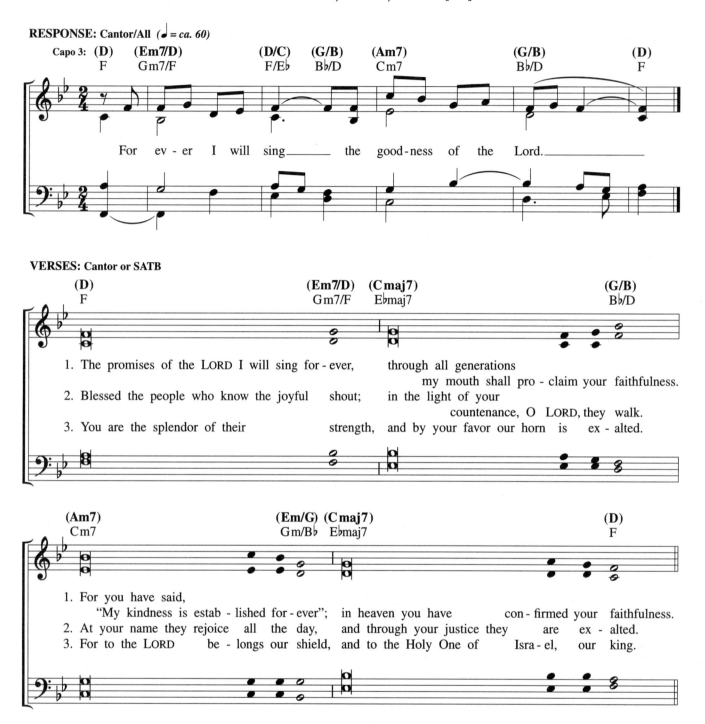

RESPONSE: Cantor/All (♩ = *ca. 60*)

For ev - er I will sing___ the good-ness of the Lord.___

VERSES: Cantor or SATB

1. The promises of the LORD I will sing for - ever, through all generations my mouth shall pro - claim your faithfulness.
2. Blessed the people who know the joyful shout; in the light of your countenance, O LORD, they walk.
3. You are the splendor of their strength, and by your favor our horn is ex - alted.

1. For you have said, "My kindness is estab - lished for - ever"; in heaven you have con - firmed your faithfulness.
2. At your name they rejoice all the day, and through your justice they are ex - alted.
3. For to the LORD be - longs our shield, and to the Holy One of Isra - el, our king.

Gospel Acclamation for this celebration may be found on page 238.
A separate assembly response may be found on page 264.

13TH SUNDAY IN ORDINARY TIME — B

Psalm 30: 2, 4, 5–6, 11, 12, 13 [98]

Gospel Acclamation for this celebration may be found on page 244.
A separate assembly response may be found on page 266.

13TH SUNDAY IN ORDINARY TIME — C

Psalm 16: 1–2, 5, 7–8, 9–10, 11 [99]

RESPONSE: Cantor/All *(♩ = ca. 95)*

You are my in-her-i-tance, O Lord.

VERSES: Cantor or SATB

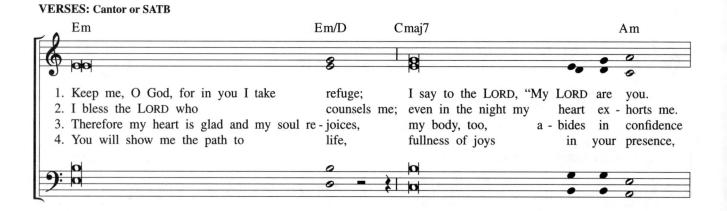

1. Keep me, O God, for in you I take refuge; I say to the LORD, "My LORD are you.
2. I bless the LORD who counsels me; even in the night my heart ex-horts me.
3. Therefore my heart is glad and my soul re-joices, my body, too, a-bides in confidence
4. You will show me the path to life, fullness of joys in your presence,

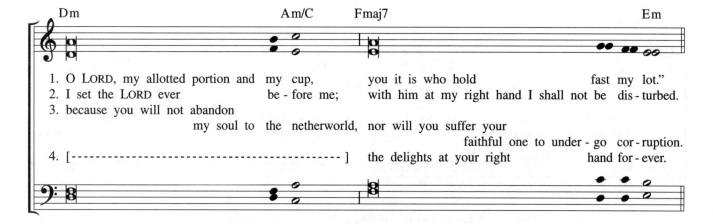

1. O LORD, my allotted portion and my cup, you it is who hold fast my lot."
2. I set the LORD ever be-fore me; with him at my right hand I shall not be dis-turbed.
3. because you will not abandon my soul to the netherworld, nor will you suffer your faithful one to under-go cor-ruption.
4. [---] the delights at your right hand for-ever.

Gospel Acclamation for this celebration may be found on page 250.
A separate assembly response may be found on page 277.

14TH SUNDAY IN ORDINARY TIME — A

Psalm 145: 1–2, 8–9, 10–11, 13–14 [100]

RESPONSE: Cantor/All (♩ = ca. 110) [or: Alleluia.]

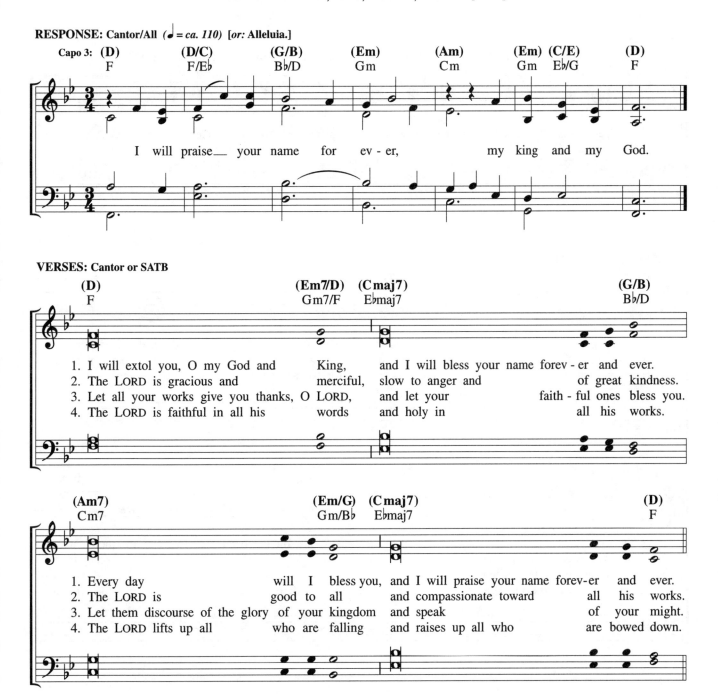

I will praise__ your name for ev-er, my king and my God.

VERSES: Cantor or SATB

1. I will extol you, O my God and King, and I will bless your name forev-er and ever.
2. The LORD is gracious and merciful, slow to anger and of great kindness.
3. Let all your works give you thanks, O LORD, and let your faith-ful ones bless you.
4. The LORD is faithful in all his words and holy in all his works.

1. Every day will I bless you, and I will praise your name forev-er and ever.
2. The LORD is good to all and compassionate toward all his works.
3. Let them discourse of the glory of your kingdom and speak of your might.
4. The LORD lifts up all who are falling and raises up all who are bowed down.

Gospel Acclamation for this celebration may be found on page 238.
A separate assembly response may be found on page 266.

14th Sunday in Ordinary Time — B

Psalm 123: 1–2, 2, 3–4 [101]

RESPONSE: Cantor/All (♩ = ca. 50)

Our eyes are fixed on the Lord,___ plead-ing for his mer - cy.___

VERSES: Cantor or SATB

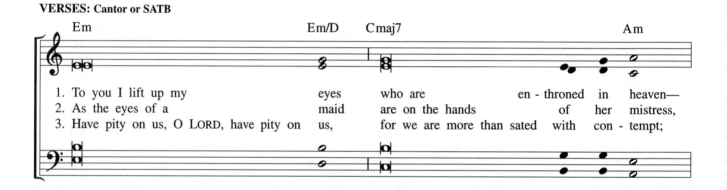

1. To you I lift up my eyes who are en - throned in heaven—
2. As the eyes of a maid are on the hands of her mistress,
3. Have pity on us, O LORD, have pity on us, for we are more than sated with con - tempt;

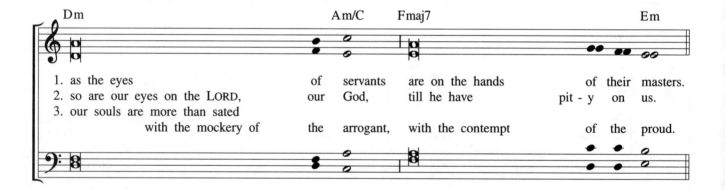

1. as the eyes of servants are on the hands of their masters.
2. so are our eyes on the LORD, our God, till he have pit - y on us.
3. our souls are more than sated with the mockery of the arrogant, with the contempt of the proud.

Gospel Acclamation for this celebration may be found on page 244.
A separate assembly response may be found on page 271.

14TH SUNDAY IN ORDINARY TIME — C

Psalm 66: 1–3, 4–5, 6–7, 16, 20 [102]

RESPONSE: Cantor/All (♩ = ca. 65)

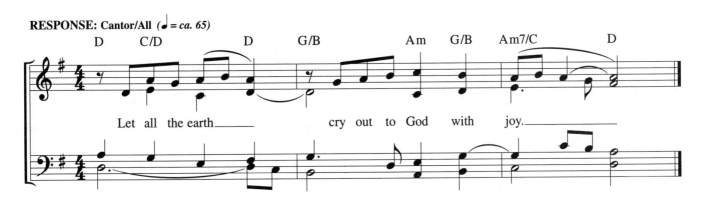

Let all the earth_____ cry out to God with joy._____

VERSES: Cantor or SATB

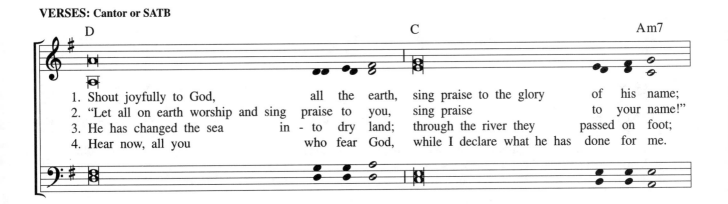

1. Shout joyfully to God, all the earth, sing praise to the glory of his name;
2. "Let all on earth worship and sing praise to you, sing praise to your name!"
3. He has changed the sea in - to dry land; through the river they passed on foot;
4. Hear now, all you who fear God, while I declare what he has done for me.

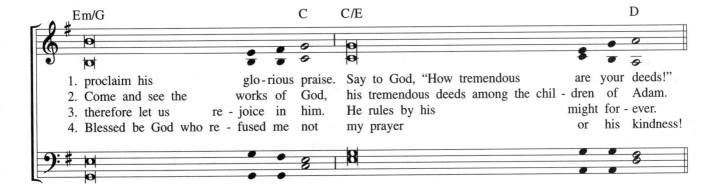

1. proclaim his glo-rious praise. Say to God, "How tremendous are your deeds!"
2. Come and see the works of God, his tremendous deeds among the chil - dren of Adam.
3. therefore let us re - joice in him. He rules by his might for - ever.
4. Blessed be God who re - fused me not my prayer or his kindness!

Music © 2001, John Schiavone. Published by OCP Publications. All rights reserved.

Gospel Acclamation for this celebration may be found on page 250.
A separate assembly response may be found on page 267.

15TH SUNDAY IN ORDINARY TIME — A

Psalm 65: 10, 11, 12–13, 14 [103]

Gospel Acclamation for this celebration may be found on page 238.
A separate assembly response may be found on page 275.

15TH SUNDAY IN ORDINARY TIME — B

Psalm 85: 9–10, 11–12, 13–14 [104]

RESPONSE: Cantor/All (♩ = ca. 85)

Lord, let us see your kind-ness, and grant us your sal-va-tion.

VERSES: Cantor or SATB

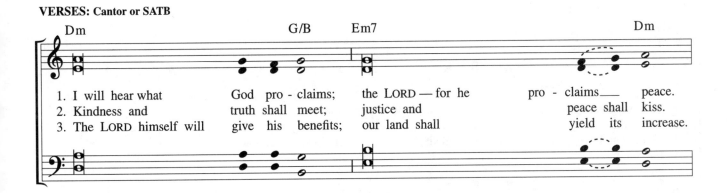

1. I will hear what God pro-claims; the LORD — for he pro-claims___ peace.
2. Kindness and truth shall meet; justice and peace shall kiss.
3. The LORD himself will give his benefits; our land shall yield its increase.

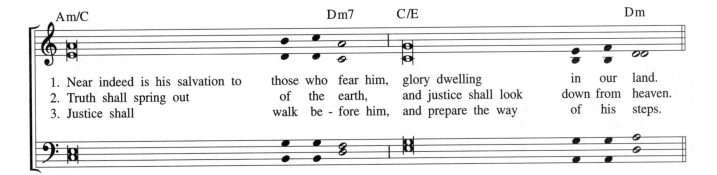

1. Near indeed is his salvation to those who fear him, glory dwelling in our land.
2. Truth shall spring out of the earth, and justice shall look down from heaven.
3. Justice shall walk be-fore him, and prepare the way of his steps.

Gospel Acclamation for this celebration may be found on page 244.
A separate assembly response may be found on page 269.

15TH SUNDAY IN ORDINARY TIME — C

Psalm 69: 14, 17, 30–31, 33–34, 36, 37 [105–1]

RESPONSE: Cantor/All (♩. = *ca. 40*)

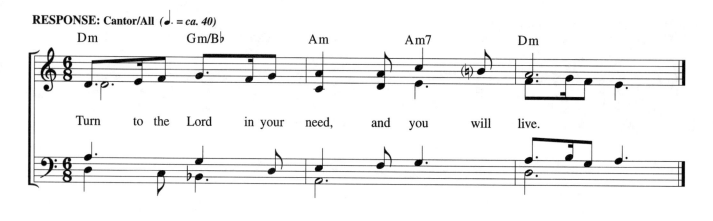

Turn to the Lord in your need, and you will live.

VERSES: Cantor or SATB

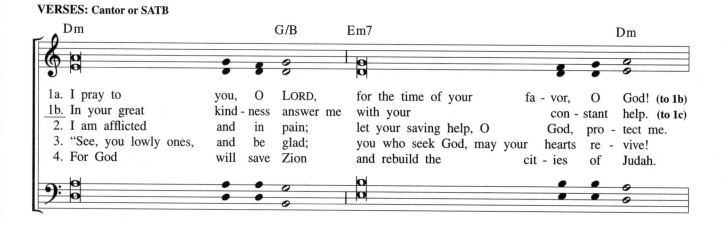

1a. I pray to you, O LORD, for the time of your fa - vor, O God! **(to 1b)**
1b. In your great kind - ness answer me with your con - stant help. **(to 1c)**
2. I am afflicted and in pain; let your saving help, O God, pro - tect me.
3. "See, you lowly ones, and be glad; you who seek God, may your hearts re - vive!
4. For God will save Zion and rebuild the cit - ies of Judah.

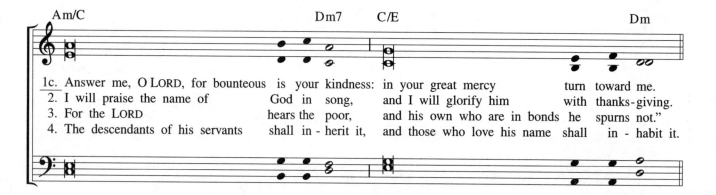

1c. Answer me, O LORD, for bounteous is your kindness: in your great mercy turn toward me.
2. I will praise the name of God in song, and I will glorify him with thanks-giving.
3. For the LORD hears the poor, and his own who are in bonds he spurns not."
4. The descendants of his servants shall in - herit it, and those who love his name shall in - habit it.

Gospel Acclamation for this celebration may be found on page 250.
A separate assembly response may be found on page 277.

15TH SUNDAY IN ORDINARY TIME — C

Psalm 19: 8, 9, 10, 11 [105–2]

OR

RESPONSE: Cantor/All (♩ = ca. 70)

Your words, Lord, are Spir - it and life.

VERSES: Cantor or SATB

1. The law of the LORD is perfect, refresh - ing the soul;
2. The precepts of the LORD are right, rejoic - ing the heart;
3. The fear of the LORD is pure, endur - ing for - ever;
4. They are more pre - cious than gold, than a heap of pur - est gold;

1. the decree of the LORD is trustworthy, giving wisdom to the simple.
2. the command of the LORD is clear, enlighten - ing the eye.
3. the ordinances of the LORD are true, all of them just.
4. sweeter al - so than syrup or honey from the comb.

Gospel Acclamation for this celebration may be found on page 250.
A separate assembly response may be found on page 278.

16TH SUNDAY IN ORDINARY TIME — A

Psalm 86: 5–6, 9–10, 15–16 [106]

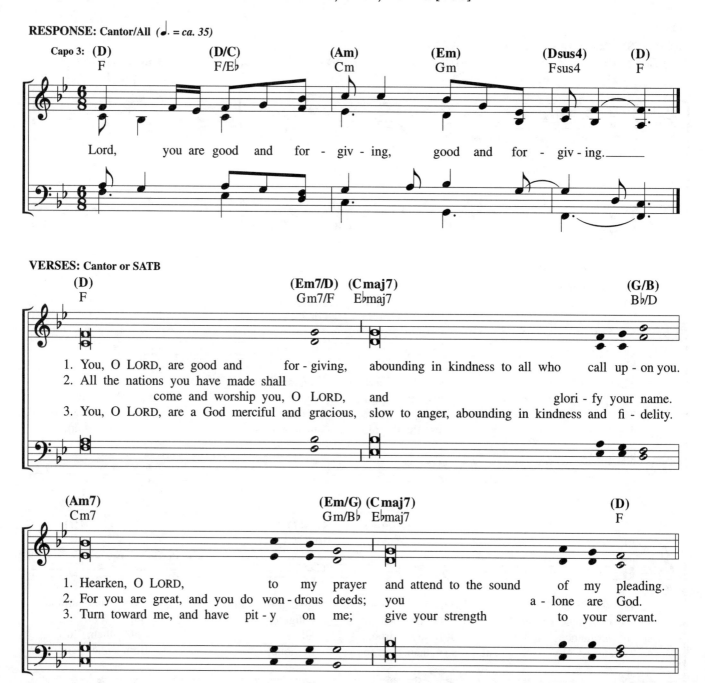

Gospel Acclamation for this celebration may be found on page 238.
A separate assembly response may be found on page 270.

16TH SUNDAY IN ORDINARY TIME — B

Psalm 23: 1–3, 3–4, 5, 6 [107]

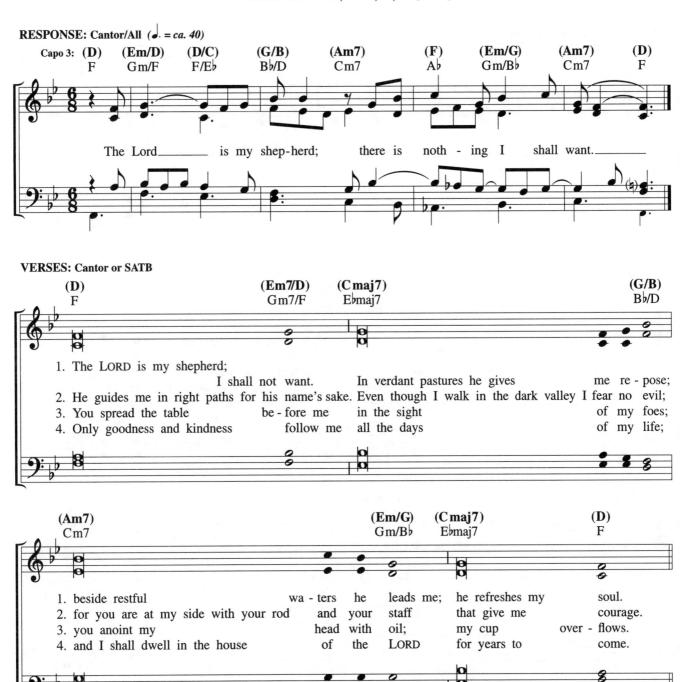

Gospel Acclamation for this celebration may be found on page 244.
A separate assembly response may be found on page 274.

16TH SUNDAY IN ORDINARY TIME — C

Psalm 15: 2–3, 3–4, 5 [108]

Gospel Acclamation for this celebration may be found on page 250.
A separate assembly response may be found on page 265.

17TH SUNDAY IN ORDINARY TIME — A

Psalm 119: 57, 72, 76–77, 127–128, 129–130 [109]

Gospel Acclamation for this celebration may be found on page 238.
A separate assembly response may be found on page 269.

17TH SUNDAY IN ORDINARY TIME — B

Psalm 145: 10–11, 15–16, 17–18 [110]

Gospel Acclamation for this celebration may be found on page 244.
A separate assembly response may be found on page 273.

17TH SUNDAY IN ORDINARY TIME — C

Psalm 138: 1–2, 2–3, 6–7, 7–8 [111]

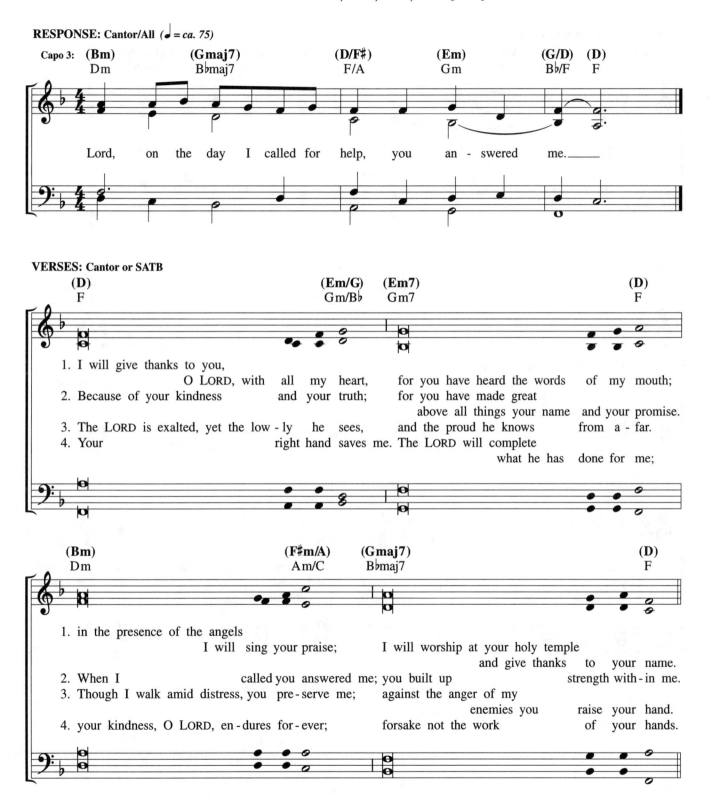

Gospel Acclamation for this celebration may be found on page 250.
A separate assembly response may be found on page 269.

18TH SUNDAY IN ORDINARY TIME — A

Psalm 145: 8–9, 15–16, 17–18 [112]

Gospel Acclamation for this celebration may be found on page 239.
A separate assembly response may be found on page 273.

18TH SUNDAY IN ORDINARY TIME — B

Psalm 78: 3–4, 23–24, 25, 54 [113]

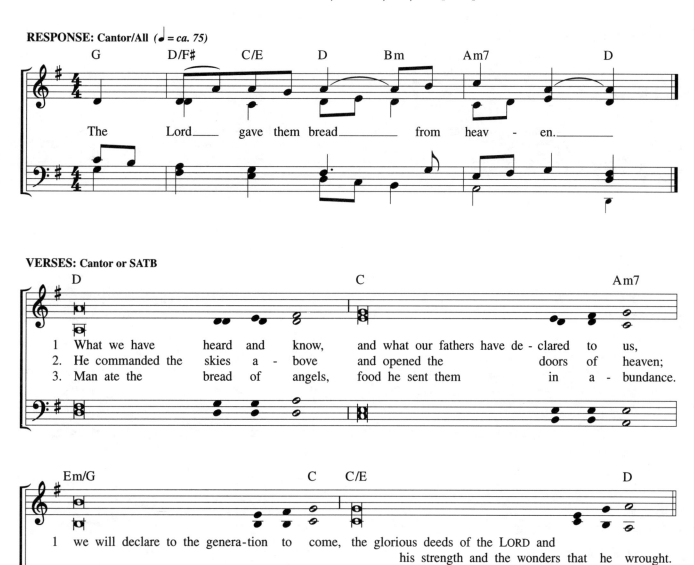

RESPONSE: Cantor/All (♩ = *ca. 75*)

The Lord gave them bread from heav - en.

VERSES: Cantor or SATB

1. What we have heard and know, and what our fathers have de - clared to us,
2. He commanded the skies a - bove and opened the doors of heaven;
3. Man ate the bread of angels, food he sent them in a - bundance.

1. we will declare to the genera-tion to come, the glorious deeds of the LORD and his strength and the wonders that he wrought.
2. he rained manna upon them for food and gave them heav - en - ly bread.
3. And he brought them to his ho - ly land, to the mountains his right hand had won.

Gospel Acclamation for this celebration may be found on page 245.
A separate assembly response may be found on page 273.

18TH SUNDAY IN ORDINARY TIME — C

Psalm 90: 3–4, 5–6, 12–13, 14, 17 [114]

RESPONSE: Cantor/All (♩ = ca. 45)

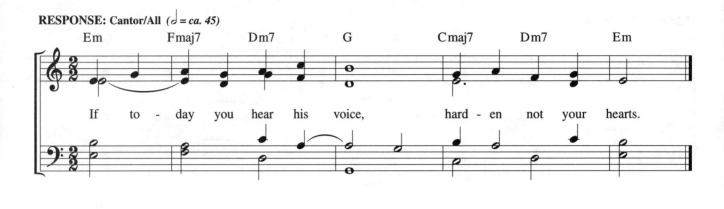

If to-day you hear his voice, hard-en not your hearts.

VERSES: Cantor or SATB

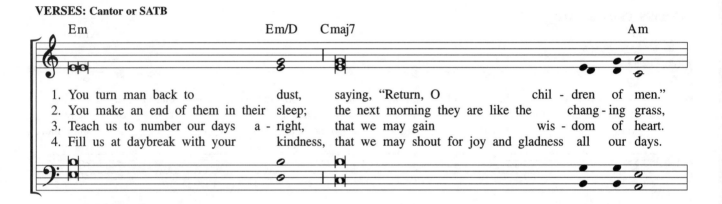

1. You turn man back to dust, saying, "Return, O chil-dren of men."
2. You make an end of them in their sleep; the next morning they are like the chang-ing grass,
3. Teach us to number our days a-right, that we may gain wis-dom of heart.
4. Fill us at daybreak with your kindness, that we may shout for joy and gladness all our days.

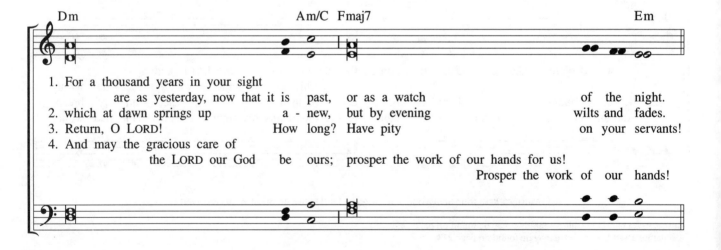

1. For a thousand years in your sight
   are as yesterday, now that it is past, or as a watch of the night.
2. which at dawn springs up a-new, but by evening wilts and fades.
3. Return, O LORD! How long? Have pity on your servants!
4. And may the gracious care of
   the LORD our God be ours; prosper the work of our hands for us!
   Prosper the work of our hands!

Gospel Acclamation for this celebration may be found on page 251.
A separate assembly response may be found on page 266.

19TH SUNDAY IN ORDINARY TIME — A

Psalm 85: 9, 10, 11–12, 13–14 [115]

RESPONSE: Cantor/All (♩ = *ca. 85*)

Lord, let us see your kind-ness, and grant us your sal-va-tion.

VERSES: Cantor or SATB

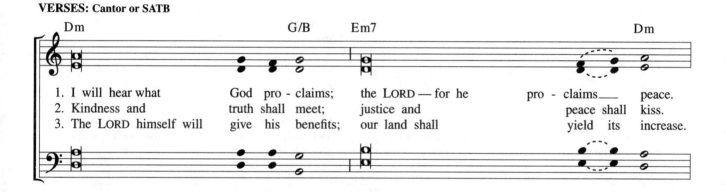

1. I will hear what God pro-claims; the LORD — for he pro-claims___ peace.
2. Kindness and truth shall meet; justice and peace shall kiss.
3. The LORD himself will give his benefits; our land shall yield its increase.

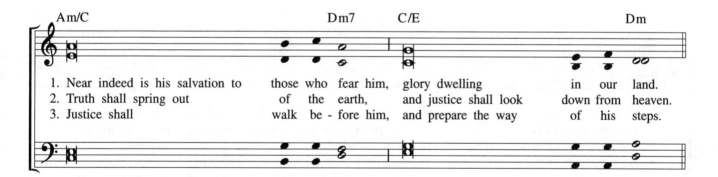

1. Near indeed is his salvation to those who fear him, glory dwelling in our land.
2. Truth shall spring out of the earth, and justice shall look down from heaven.
3. Justice shall walk be-fore him, and prepare the way of his steps.

Gospel Acclamation for this celebration may be found on page 239.
A separate assembly response may be found on page 269.

19TH SUNDAY IN ORDINARY TIME — B

Psalm 34: 2–3, 4–5, 6–7, 8–9 [116]

Gospel Acclamation for this celebration may be found on page 245.
A separate assembly response may be found on page 272.

19TH SUNDAY IN ORDINARY TIME — C

Psalm 33: 1, 12, 18–19, 20–22 [117]

RESPONSE: Cantor/All (♩ = *ca. 85*)

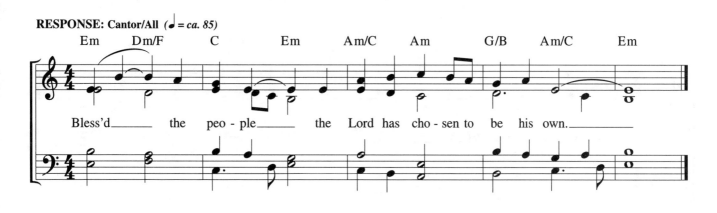

Bless'd___ the peo-ple___ the Lord has cho-sen to be his own.___

VERSES: Cantor or SATB

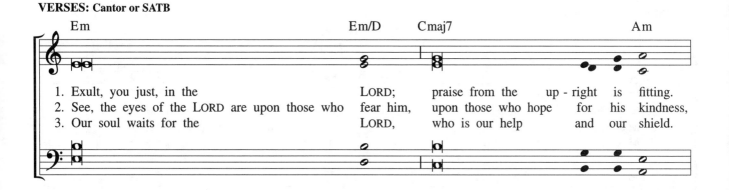

1. Exult, you just, in the LORD; praise from the up-right is fitting.
2. See, the eyes of the LORD are upon those who fear him, upon those who hope for his kindness,
3. Our soul waits for the LORD, who is our help and our shield.

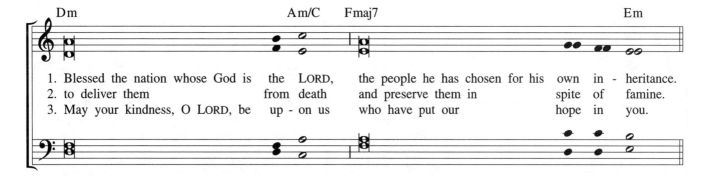

1. Blessed the nation whose God is the LORD, the people he has chosen for his own in-heritance.
2. to deliver them from death and preserve them in spite of famine.
3. May your kindness, O LORD, be up-on us who have put our hope in you.

Gospel Acclamation for this celebration may be found on page 251.
A separate assembly response may be found on page 263.

20TH SUNDAY IN ORDINARY TIME — A

Psalm 67: 2–3, 5, 6, 8 [118]

Gospel Acclamation for this celebration may be found on page 239.
A separate assembly response may be found on page 271.

20TH SUNDAY IN ORDINARY TIME — B

Psalm 34: 2–3, 4–5, 6–7 [119]

Gospel Acclamation for this celebration may be found on page 245.
A separate assembly response may be found on page 272.

20TH SUNDAY IN ORDINARY TIME — C

Psalm 40: 2, 3, 4, 18 [120]

RESPONSE: Cantor/All (♩ = *ca. 70*)

Lord,— Lord,— come to my aid! Come to my aid!_____

VERSES: Cantor or SATB

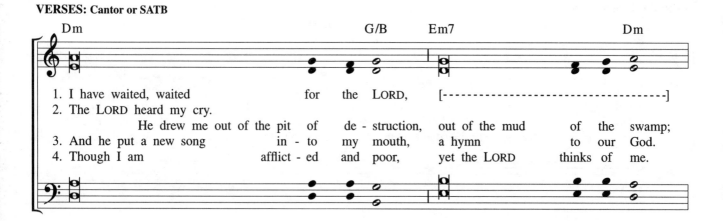

1. I have waited, waited for the LORD, [--]
2. The LORD heard my cry.
   He drew me out of the pit of de-struction, out of the mud of the swamp;
3. And he put a new song in-to my mouth, a hymn to our God.
4. Though I am afflict-ed and poor, yet the LORD thinks of me.

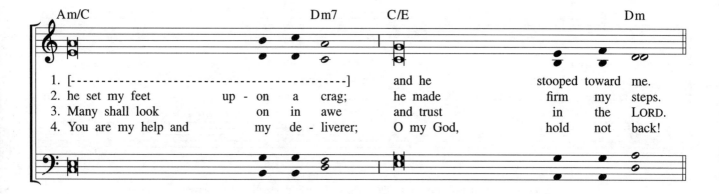

1. [--] and he stooped toward me.
2. he set my feet up-on a crag; he made firm my steps.
3. Many shall look on in awe and trust in the LORD.
4. You are my help and my de-liverer; O my God, hold not back!

Gospel Acclamation for this celebration may be found on page 251.
A separate assembly response may be found on page 268.

21ST SUNDAY IN ORDINARY TIME — A

Psalm 138: 1–2, 2–3, 6, 8 [121]

Gospel Acclamation for this celebration may be found on page 239.
A separate assembly response may be found on page 270.

21ST SUNDAY IN ORDINARY TIME — B

Psalm 34: 2–3, 16–17, 18–19, 20–21 [122]

Gospel Acclamation for this celebration may be found on page 245.
A separate assembly response may be found on page 272.

21ST SUNDAY IN ORDINARY TIME — C

Psalm 117: 1, 2 [123]

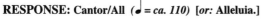

RESPONSE: Cantor/All (♩ = *ca. 110*) [*or:* Alleluia.]

Go out to all the world and tell the Good News.

VERSES: Cantor or SATB

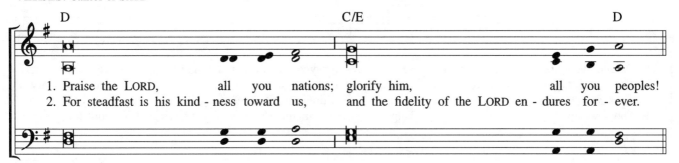

1. Praise the LORD, all you nations; glorify him, all you peoples!
2. For steadfast is his kind-ness toward us, and the fidelity of the LORD en-dures for-ever.

Gospel Acclamation for this celebration may be found on page 251.
A separate assembly response may be found on page 264.

22ND SUNDAY IN ORDINARY TIME — A

Psalm 63: 2, 3–4, 5–6, 8–9 [124]

RESPONSE: Cantor/All (♩ = ca. 42)

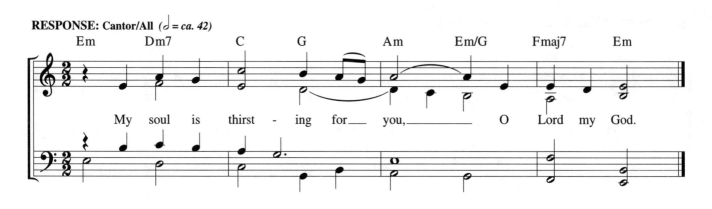

My soul is thirst - ing for you, O Lord my God.

VERSES: Cantor or SATB

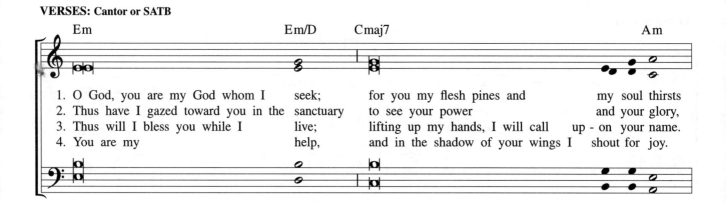

1. O God, you are my God whom I seek; for you my flesh pines and my soul thirsts
2. Thus have I gazed toward you in the sanctuary to see your power and your glory,
3. Thus will I bless you while I live; lifting up my hands, I will call up - on your name.
4. You are my help, and in the shadow of your wings I shout for joy.

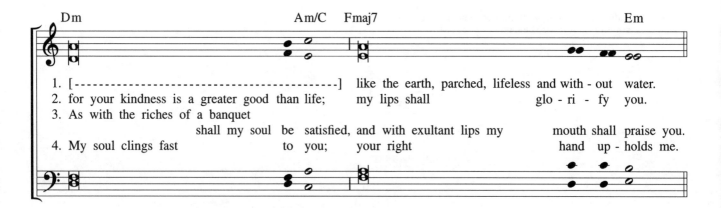

1. [--] like the earth, parched, lifeless and with - out water.
2. for your kindness is a greater good than life; my lips shall glo - ri - fy you.
3. As with the riches of a banquet shall my soul be satisfied, and with exultant lips my mouth shall praise you.
4. My soul clings fast to you; your right hand up - holds me.

Gospel Acclamation for this celebration may be found on page 239.
A separate assembly response may be found on page 270.

22ND SUNDAY IN ORDINARY TIME — B

Psalm 15: 2–3, 3–4, 4–5 [125]

RESPONSE: Cantor/All (♩. = *ca. 30*)

The one who does jus-tice will live in the pres-ence of the Lord.

VERSES: Cantor or SATB

1. Whoever walks blamelessly and does justice; who thinks the truth in his heart
2. Who harms not his fel-low man, nor takes up a reproach a-gainst his neighbor;
3. Who lends not his mon-ey at usury and accepts no bribe a-gainst the innocent.

1. [--] and slanders not with his tongue.
2. by whom the reprobate is de-spised, while he honors those who fear the LORD.
3. Whoever does these things shall never be dis-turbed.

Gospel Acclamation for this celebration may be found on page 245.
A separate assembly response may be found on page 275.

22ND SUNDAY IN ORDINARY TIME — C

Psalm 68: 4–5, 6–7, 10–11 [126]

RESPONSE: Cantor/All (♩ = *ca. 75*)

God,_____ in your good - ness, you have made a home for the poor.

VERSES: Cantor or SATB

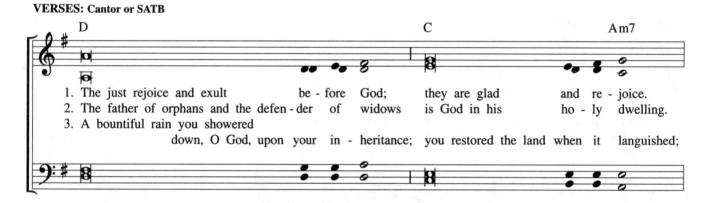

1. The just rejoice and exult be - fore God; they are glad and re - joice.
2. The father of orphans and the defen - der of widows is God in his ho - ly dwelling.
3. A bountiful rain you showered down, O God, upon your in - heritance; you restored the land when it languished;

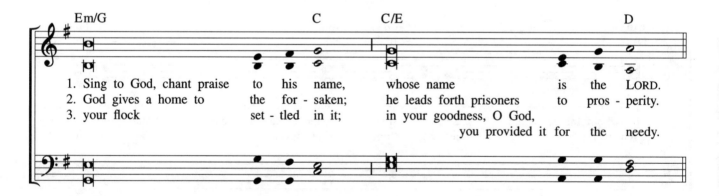

1. Sing to God, chant praise to his name, whose name is the LORD.
2. God gives a home to the for - saken; he leads forth prisoners to pros - perity.
3. your flock set - tled in it; in your goodness, O God, you provided it for the needy.

Gospel Acclamation for this celebration may be found on page 251.
A separate assembly response may be found on page 264.

23RD SUNDAY IN ORDINARY TIME — A

Psalm 95: 1–2, 6–7, 8–9 [127]

RESPONSE: Cantor/All (♩ = *ca. 45*)

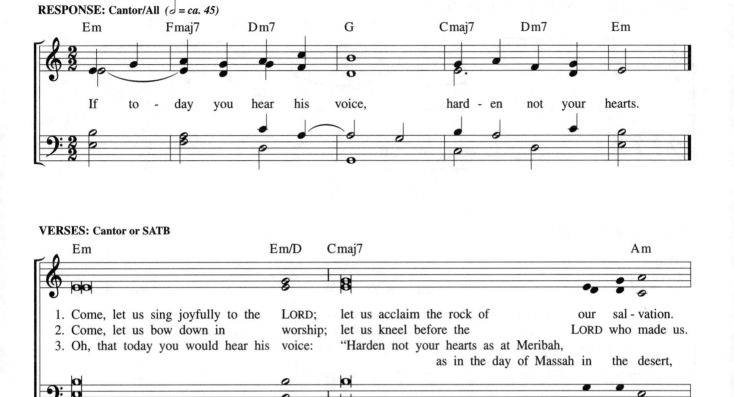

If to-day you hear his voice, hard-en not your hearts.

VERSES: Cantor or SATB

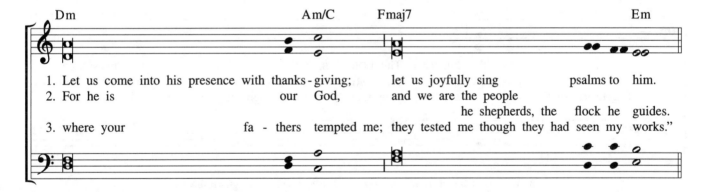

1. Come, let us sing joyfully to the LORD; let us acclaim the rock of our sal-vation.
2. Come, let us bow down in worship; let us kneel before the LORD who made us.
3. Oh, that today you would hear his voice: "Harden not your hearts as at Meribah, as in the day of Massah in the desert,

1. Let us come into his presence with thanks-giving; let us joyfully sing psalms to him.
2. For he is our God, and we are the people he shepherds, the flock he guides.
3. where your fa-thers tempted me; they tested me though they had seen my works."

Gospel Acclamation for this celebration may be found on page 239.
A separate assembly response may be found on page 266.

23RD SUNDAY IN ORDINARY TIME — B

Psalm 146: 7, 8–9, 9–10 [128]

RESPONSE: Cantor/All (♩ = ca. 70) [or: Alleluia.]

Praise_____ the Lord,_____ my soul,_____ my soul!

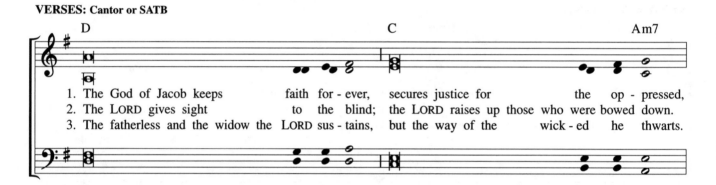

VERSES: Cantor or SATB

1. The God of Jacob keeps faith for - ever, secures justice for the op - pressed,
2. The LORD gives sight to the blind; the LORD raises up those who were bowed down.
3. The fatherless and the widow the LORD sus - tains, but the way of the wick - ed he thwarts.

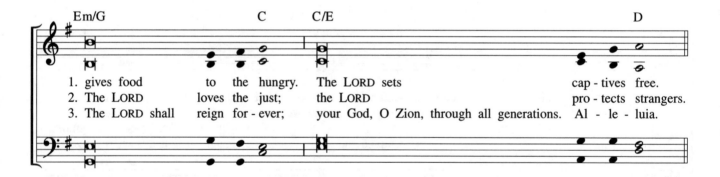

1. gives food to the hungry. The LORD sets cap - tives free.
2. The LORD loves the just; the LORD pro - tects strangers.
3. The LORD shall reign for - ever; your God, O Zion, through all generations. Al - le - luia.

Gospel Acclamation for this celebration may be found on page 245.
A separate assembly response may be found on page 272.

23RD SUNDAY IN ORDINARY TIME — C

Psalm 90: 3–4, 5–6, 12–13, 14–17 [129]

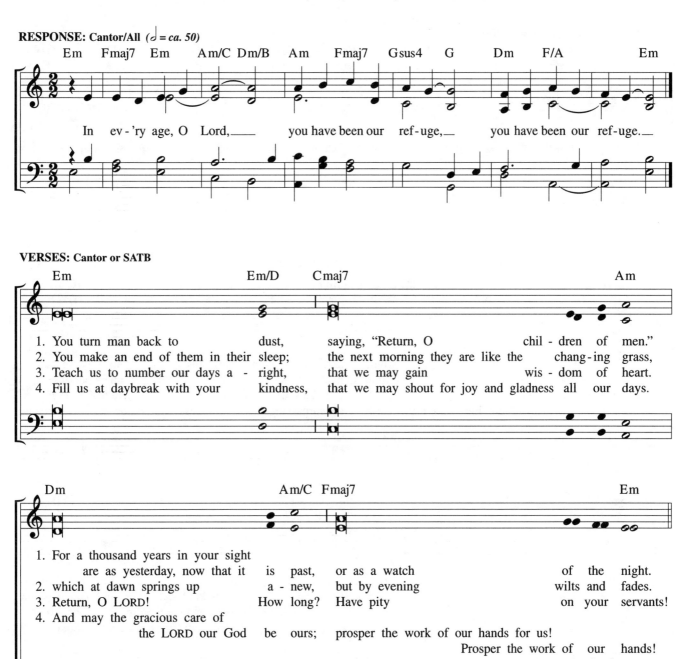

RESPONSE: Cantor/All (♩ = ca. 50)

In ev-'ry age, O Lord,___ you have been our ref-uge,___ you have been our ref-uge.___

VERSES: Cantor or SATB

1. You turn man back to dust, saying, "Return, O chil - dren of men."
2. You make an end of them in their sleep; the next morning they are like the chang-ing grass,
3. Teach us to number our days a - right, that we may gain wis - dom of heart.
4. Fill us at daybreak with your kindness, that we may shout for joy and gladness all our days.

1. For a thousand years in your sight are as yesterday, now that it is past, or as a watch of the night.
2. which at dawn springs up a - new, but by evening wilts and fades.
3. Return, O LORD! How long? Have pity on your servants!
4. And may the gracious care of the LORD our God be ours; prosper the work of our hands for us! Prosper the work of our hands!

Gospel Acclamation for this celebration may be found on page 251.
A separate assembly response may be found on page 267.

24TH SUNDAY IN ORDINARY TIME — A

Psalm 103: 1–2, 3–4, 9–10, 11–12 [130]

RESPONSE: Cantor/All (♩ = *ca. 110*)

The Lord is kind and mer-ci-ful, slow to an-ger, and rich in com-pas-sion.

VERSES: Cantor or SATB

1. Bless the LORD, O my soul; and all my being, bless his ho-ly name.
2. He pardons all your in-iquities, heals all your ills.
3. He will not always chide, nor does he keep his wrath for-ever.
4. For as the heavens are high above the earth, so surpassing is his kindness toward those who fear him.

1. Bless the LORD, O my soul, and forget not all his benefits.
2. He redeems your life from de-struction, crowns you with kindness and com-passion.
3. Not according to our sins does he deal with us, nor does he requite us according to our crimes.
4. As far as the east is from the west, so far has he put our transgres-sions from us.

Gospel Acclamation for this celebration may be found on page 240.
A separate assembly response may be found on page 274.

24TH SUNDAY IN ORDINARY TIME — B

Psalm 116: 1–2, 3–4, 5–6, 8–9 [131]

RESPONSE: Cantor/All (♩ = ca. 80) [or: Alleluia.]

VERSES: Cantor or SATB

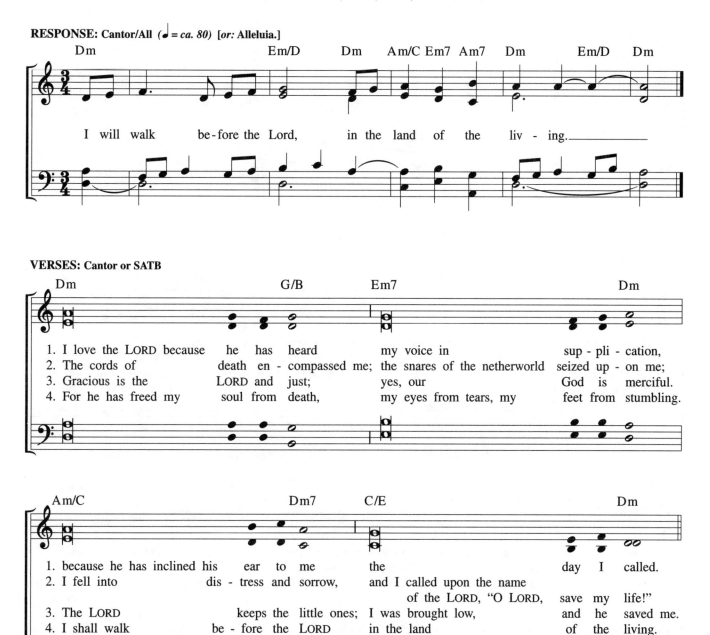

1. I love the LORD because he has heard my voice in sup - pli - cation,
2. The cords of death en - compassed me; the snares of the netherworld seized up - on me;
3. Gracious is the LORD and just; yes, our God is merciful.
4. For he has freed my soul from death, my eyes from tears, my feet from stumbling.

1. because he has inclined his ear to me the day I called.
2. I fell into dis - tress and sorrow, and I called upon the name of the LORD, "O LORD, save my life!"
3. The LORD keeps the little ones; I was brought low, and he saved me.
4. I shall walk be - fore the LORD in the land of the living.

Gospel Acclamation for this celebration may be found on page 246.
A separate assembly response may be found on page 266.

24TH SUNDAY IN ORDINARY TIME — C

Psalm 51: 3–4, 12–13, 17, 19 [132]

RESPONSE: Cantor/All (♩ = *ca. 75*)

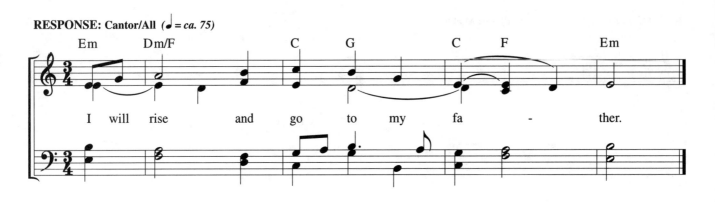

I will rise and go to my fa - ther.

VERSES: Cantor or SATB

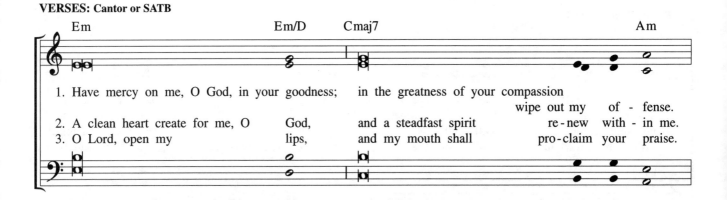

1. Have mercy on me, O God, in your goodness; in the greatness of your compassion wipe out my of - fense.
2. A clean heart create for me, O God, and a steadfast spirit re - new with - in me.
3. O Lord, open my lips, and my mouth shall pro - claim your praise.

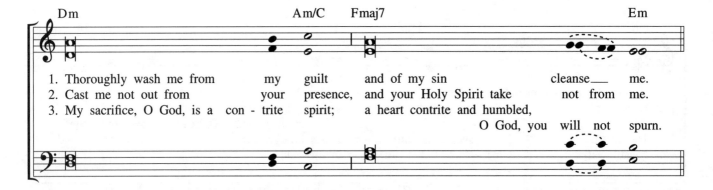

1. Thoroughly wash me from my guilt and of my sin cleanse___ me.
2. Cast me not out from your presence, and your Holy Spirit take not from me.
3. My sacrifice, O God, is a con - trite spirit; a heart contrite and humbled, O God, you will not spurn.

Gospel Acclamation for this celebration may be found on page 252.
A separate assembly response may be found on page 266.

25TH SUNDAY IN ORDINARY TIME — A

Psalm 145: 2–3, 8–9, 17–18 [133]

Gospel Acclamation for this celebration may be found on page 240.
A separate assembly response may be found on page 274.

25TH SUNDAY IN ORDINARY TIME — B

Psalm 54: 3–4, 5, 6–8 [134]

RESPONSE: Cantor/All (♩ = *ca. 45*)

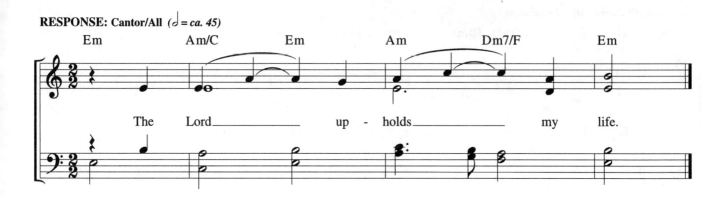

The Lord_____ up - holds_____ my life.

VERSES: Cantor or SATB

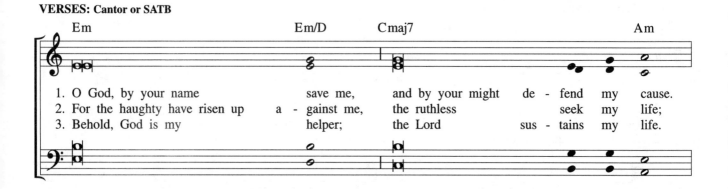

1. O God, by your name save me, and by your might de - fend my cause.
2. For the haughty have risen up a - gainst me, the ruthless seek my life;
3. Behold, God is my helper; the Lord sus - tains my life.

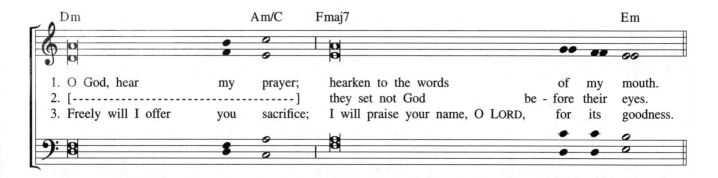

1. O God, hear my prayer; hearken to the words of my mouth.
2. [----------------------------------] they set not God be - fore their eyes.
3. Freely will I offer you sacrifice; I will praise your name, O LORD, for its goodness.

Gospel Acclamation for this celebration may be found on page 246.
A separate assembly response may be found on page 275.

25TH SUNDAY IN ORDINARY TIME — C

Psalm 113: 1–2, 4–6, 7–8 [135]

RESPONSE: Cantor/All (♩ = *ca. 95*) [*or:* Alleluia.]

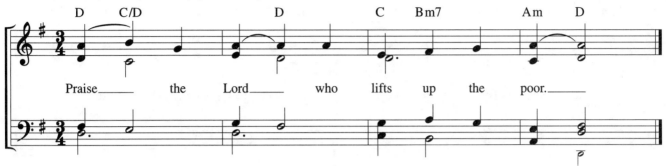

Praise the Lord who lifts up the poor.

VERSES: Cantor or SATB

1. Praise, you servants of the LORD, praise the name of the LORD.
2. High above all nations is the LORD; above the heavens is his glory.
3. He raises up the lowly from the dust; from the dunghill he lifts up the poor

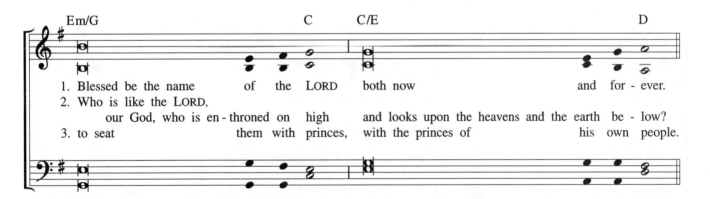

1. Blessed be the name of the LORD both now and for-ever.
2. Who is like the LORD,
   our God, who is en-throned on high and looks upon the heavens and the earth be-low?
3. to seat them with princes, with the princes of his own people.

Gospel Acclamation for this celebration may be found on page 252.
A separate assembly response may be found on page 272.

26TH SUNDAY IN ORDINARY TIME — A

Psalm 25: 4–5, 6–7, 8–9 [136]

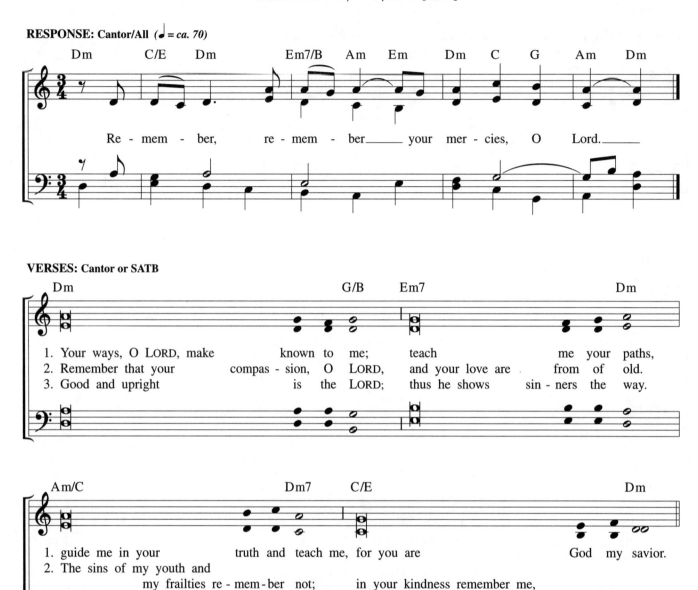

Gospel Acclamation for this celebration may be found on page 240.
A separate assembly response may be found on page 272.

26TH SUNDAY IN ORDINARY TIME — B

Psalm 19: 8, 10, 12–13, 14 [137]

Gospel Acclamation for this celebration may be found on page 246.
A separate assembly response may be found on page 275.

26TH SUNDAY IN ORDINARY TIME — C

Psalm 146: 7, 8–9, 9–10 [138]

RESPONSE: Cantor/All (♩ = ca. 70) [or: Alleluia.]

Praise the Lord, my soul, my soul!

VERSES: Cantor or SATB

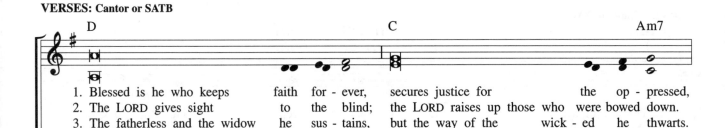

1. Blessed is he who keeps faith for - ever, secures justice for the op - pressed,
2. The LORD gives sight to the blind; the LORD raises up those who were bowed down.
3. The fatherless and the widow he sus - tains, but the way of the wick - ed he thwarts.

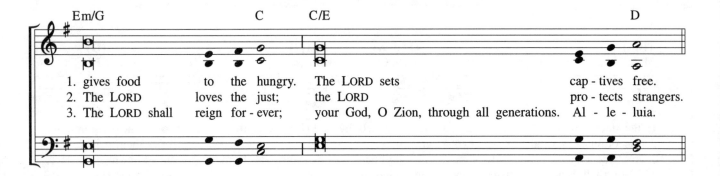

1. gives food to the hungry. The LORD sets cap - tives free.
2. The LORD loves the just; the LORD pro - tects strangers.
3. The LORD shall reign for - ever; your God, O Zion, through all generations. Al - le - luia.

Gospel Acclamation for this celebration may be found on page 252.
A separate assembly response may be found on page 272.

27th Sunday in Ordinary Time — A

Psalm 80: 9, 12, 13–14, 15–16, 19–20 [139]

RESPONSE: Cantor/All (♩ = *ca. 85*)

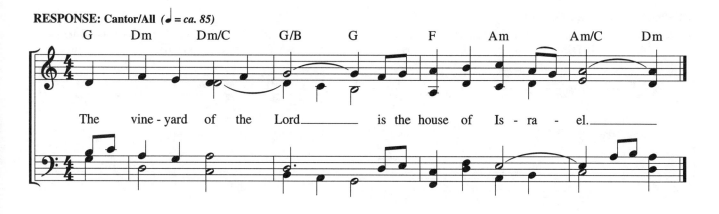

The vine-yard of the Lord_____ is the house of Is-ra-el._____

VERSES: Cantor or SATB

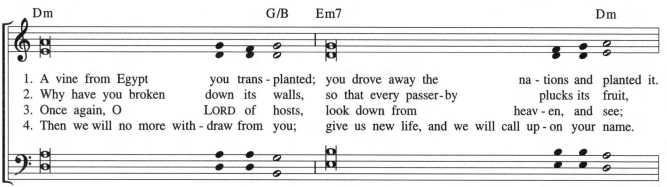

1. A vine from Egypt you trans-planted; you drove away the na-tions and planted it.
2. Why have you broken down its walls, so that every passer-by plucks its fruit,
3. Once again, O LORD of hosts, look down from heav-en, and see;
4. Then we will no more with-draw from you; give us new life, and we will call up-on your name.

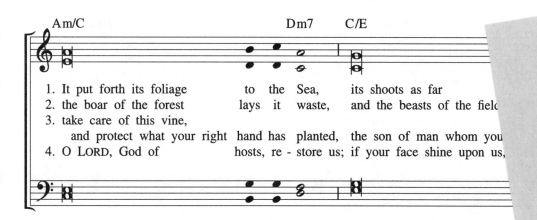

1. It put forth its foliage to the Sea, its shoots as far
2. the boar of the forest lays it waste, and the beasts of the field
3. take care of this vine,
   and protect what your right hand has planted, the son of man whom you
4. O LORD, God of hosts, re-store us; if your face shine upon us,

Gospel Acclamation for this celebration may be found on page 240.
A separate assembly response may be found on page 275.

27TH SUNDAY IN ORDINARY TIME — B

Psalm 128: 1–2, 3, 4–5, 6 [140]

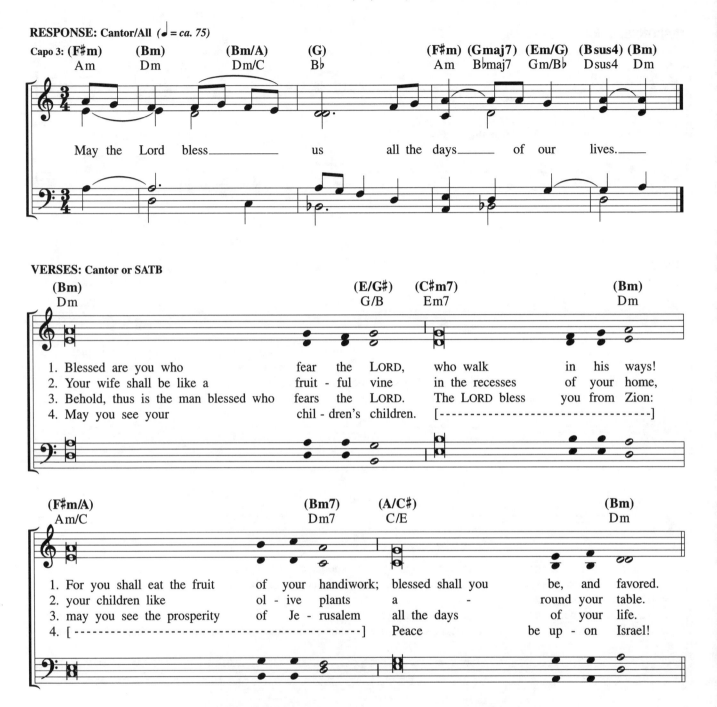

RESPONSE: Cantor/All (♩ = ca. 75)

May the Lord bless us all the days of our lives.

VERSES: Cantor or SATB

1. Blessed are you who fear the LORD, who walk in his ways!
2. Your wife shall be like a fruit-ful vine in the recesses of your home,
3. Behold, thus is the man blessed who fears the LORD. The LORD bless you from Zion:
4. May you see your chil-dren's children. [-----------------------------------]

1. For you shall eat the fruit of your handiwork; blessed shall you be, and favored.
2. your children like ol-ive plants a - round your table.
3. may you see the prosperity of Je-rusalem all the days of your life.
4. [---] Peace be up-on Israel!

Music © 2001, John Schiavone. Published by OCP Publications. All rights reserved.

Gospel Acclamation for this celebration may be found on page 246.
A separate assembly response may be found on page 270.

27TH SUNDAY IN ORDINARY TIME — C

Psalm 95: 1–2, 6–7, 8–9 [141]

RESPONSE: Cantor/All (♩ = *ca. 45*)

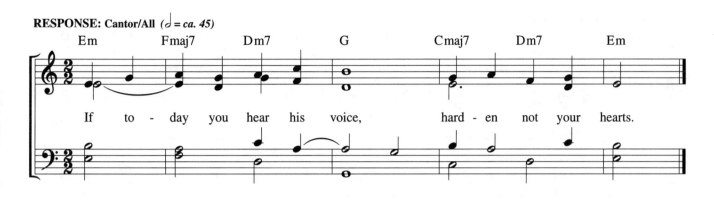

If to-day you hear his voice, hard-en not your hearts.

VERSES: Cantor or SATB

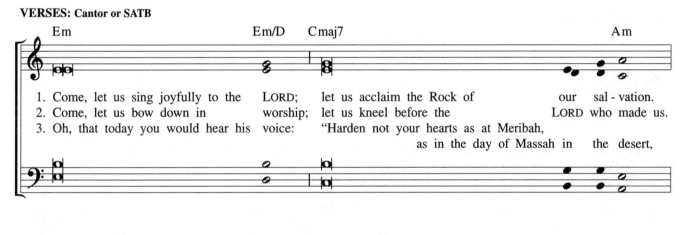

1. Come, let us sing joyfully to the LORD; let us acclaim the Rock of our sal-vation.
2. Come, let us bow down in worship; let us kneel before the LORD who made us.
3. Oh, that today you would hear his voice: "Harden not your hearts as at Meribah, as in the day of Massah in the desert,

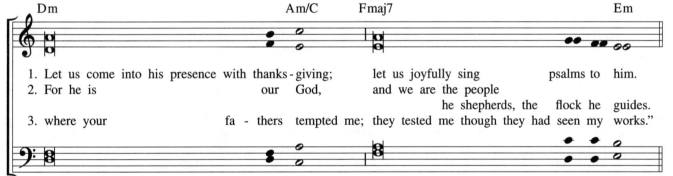

1. Let us come into his presence with thanks-giving; let us joyfully sing psalms to him.
2. For he is our God, and we are the people he shepherds, the flock he guides.
3. where your fa-thers tempted me; they tested me though they had seen my works."

Gospel Acclamation for this celebration may be found on page 252.
A separate assembly response may be found on page 266.

28TH SUNDAY IN ORDINARY TIME — A

Psalm 23: 1–3a, 3b–4, 5, 6 [142]

Gospel Acclamation for this celebration may be found on page 240.
A separate assembly response may be found on page 265.

28TH SUNDAY IN ORDINARY TIME — B

Psalm 90: 12–13, 14–15, 16–17 [143]

RESPONSE: Cantor/All (♩ = *ca. 45*)

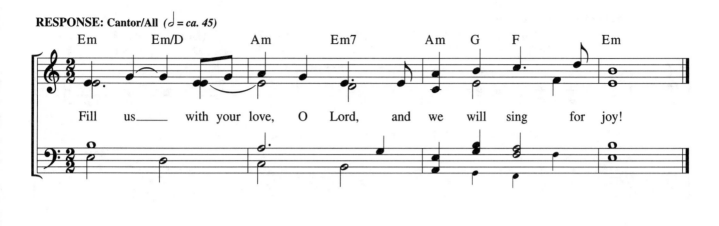

Fill us___ with your love, O Lord, and we will sing for joy!

VERSES: Cantor or SATB

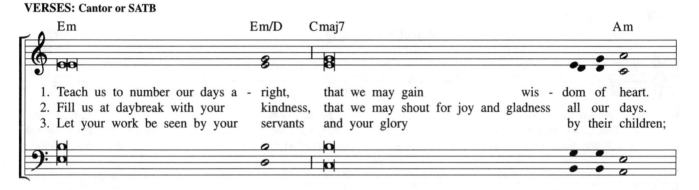

1. Teach us to number our days a - right, that we may gain wis - dom of heart.
2. Fill us at daybreak with your kindness, that we may shout for joy and gladness all our days.
3. Let your work be seen by your servants and your glory by their children;

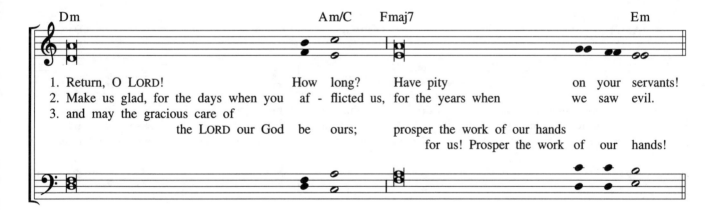

1. Return, O LORD! How long? Have pity on your servants!
2. Make us glad, for the days when you af - flicted us, for the years when we saw evil.
3. and may the gracious care of the LORD our God be ours; prosper the work of our hands for us! Prosper the work of our hands!

Gospel Acclamation for this celebration may be found on page 246.
A separate assembly response may be found on page 263.

28TH SUNDAY IN ORDINARY TIME — C

Psalm 98: 1, 2–3, 3–4 [144]

RESPONSE: Cantor/All (♩. = ca. 50)

The Lord has re-vealed to the na-tions his sav - ing pow-er.

VERSES: Cantor or SATB

1. Sing to the LORD a new song, for he has done won-drous deeds;
2. The LORD has made his salvation known: in the sight of the nations he has re - vealed his justice.
3. All the ends of the earth have seen the salvation by our God.

1. his right hand has won vic - t'ry for him, his ho - ly arm.
2. He has remembered his kindness and his faithfulness toward the house of Israel.
3. Sing joyfully to the LORD, all you lands: break into song; sing praise.

Gospel Acclamation for this celebration may be found on page 252.
A separate assembly response may be found on page 273.

29TH SUNDAY IN ORDINARY TIME — A

Psalm 96: 1, 3, 4–5, 7–8, 9–10 [145]

RESPONSE: Cantor/All (♩ = *ca. 90*)

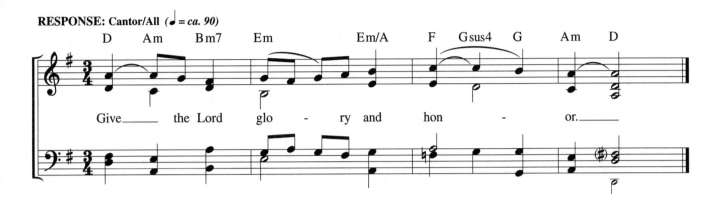

Give_____ the Lord glo - ry and hon - or._____

VERSES: Cantor or SATB

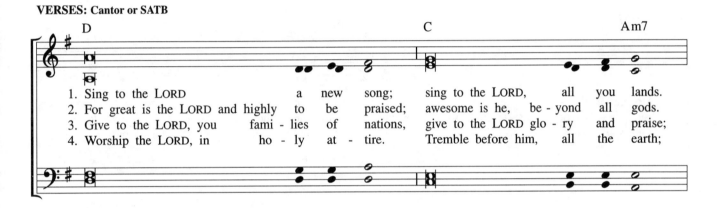

1. Sing to the LORD   a   new   song;   sing to the LORD,   all   you   lands.
2. For great is the LORD and highly   to   be   praised;   awesome is he,   be - yond   all   gods.
3. Give to the LORD, you   fami - lies   of   nations,   give to the LORD glo - ry   and   praise;
4. Worship the LORD, in   ho - ly   at - tire.   Tremble before him,   all   the   earth;

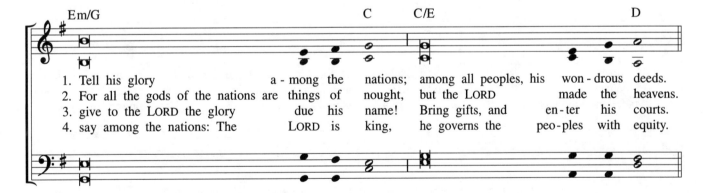

1. Tell his glory   a - mong the   nations;   among all peoples, his   won - drous   deeds.
2. For all the gods of the nations are   things of   nought,   but the LORD   made   the   heavens.
3. give to the LORD the glory   due   his   name!   Bring gifts, and   en - ter   his   courts.
4. say among the nations: The   LORD   is   king,   he governs the   peo - ples   with   equity.

Gospel Acclamation for this celebration may be found on page 241.
A separate assembly response may be found on page 264.

29TH SUNDAY IN ORDINARY TIME — B

Psalm 33: 4–5, 18–19, 20, 22 [146]

RESPONSE: Cantor/All (♩ = ca. 85)

Lord, let your mer-cy be on us,_____ as we place our trust in you.____

VERSES: Cantor or SATB

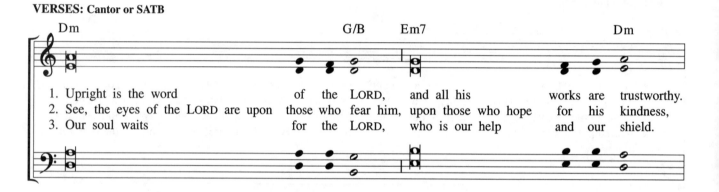

1. Upright is the word of the LORD, and all his works are trustworthy.
2. See, the eyes of the LORD are upon those who fear him, upon those who hope for his kindness,
3. Our soul waits for the LORD, who is our help and our shield.

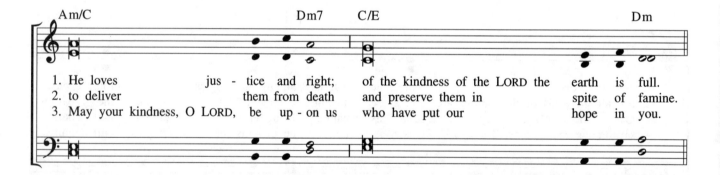

1. He loves jus-tice and right; of the kindness of the LORD the earth is full.
2. to deliver them from death and preserve them in spite of famine.
3. May your kindness, O LORD, be up-on us who have put our hope in you.

Gospel Acclamation for this celebration may be found on page 247.
A separate assembly response may be found on page 269.

29TH SUNDAY IN ORDINARY TIME — C

Psalm 121: 1–2, 3–4, 5–6, 7–8 [147]

RESPONSE: Cantor/All (♩ = ca. 50)

Our help is from the Lord, who made heav-en___ and earth.

VERSES: Cantor or SATB

1. I lift up my eyes toward the mountains; whence shall help come to me?
2. May he not suffer your foot to slip; may he slumber not who guards you:
3. The LORD is your guardian; the LORD is your shade; he is beside you at your right hand.
4. The LORD will guard you from all evil; he will guard your life.

1. My help is from the LORD, who made heav-en and earth.
2. indeed he neither slum-bers nor sleeps, the guard-ian of Israel.
3. The sun shall not harm you by day, nor the moon by night.
4. The LORD will guard your coming and your going, both now and for-ever.

Gospel Acclamation for this celebration may be found on page 253.
A separate assembly response may be found on page 271.

30TH SUNDAY IN ORDINARY TIME — A

Psalm 18: 2–3, 3–4, 47, 51 [148]

RESPONSE: Cantor/All (♩ = ca. 80)

I love you, I love you, Lord, my strength.

VERSES: Cantor or SATB

1. I love you, O LORD, my strength, [--]
2. My God, my rock of refuge, my shield, the horn of my salva-tion, my stronghold!
3. The LORD lives and blessed be my rock! Extolled be God my savior.

1. [---] O LORD, my rock, my fortress, my de-liverer.
2. Praised be the LORD, I ex-claim, and I am safe from my enemies.
3. You who gave great victories to your king and showed kindness to your a-nointed.

Gospel Acclamation for this celebration may be found on page 241.
A separate assembly response may be found on page 265.

30TH SUNDAY IN ORDINARY TIME — B

Psalm 126: 1–2, 2–3, 4–5, 6 [149]

RESPONSE: Cantor/All (♩. = ca. 40)

The Lord has done great things for us; we are filled with joy.

VERSES: Cantor or SATB

1. When the LORD brought back the captives of Zion, we were like men dreaming.
2. Then they said among the nations, "The LORD has done great things for them."
3. Restore our fortunes, O LORD, like the torrents in the south-ern desert.
4. Although they go forth weeping, carrying the seed to be sown,

1. Then our mouth was filled with laughter, and our tongue with re-joicing.
2. The LORD has done great things for us; we are glad in-deed.
3. Those that sow in tears shall reap re-joicing.
4. they shall come back re-joicing, carry - ing their sheaves.

Gospel Acclamation for this celebration may be found on page 247.
A separate assembly response may be found on page 273.

30th Sunday in Ordinary Time — C

Psalm 34: 2–3, 17–18, 19, 23 [150]

Gospel Acclamation for this celebration may be found on page 253.
A separate assembly response may be found on page 274.

31ST SUNDAY IN ORDINARY TIME — A

Psalm 131: 1, 2, 3 [151]

RESPONSE: Cantor/All (♩ = ca. 80)

In you, Lord, I have found my peace, I have found my peace.

VERSES: Cantor or SATB

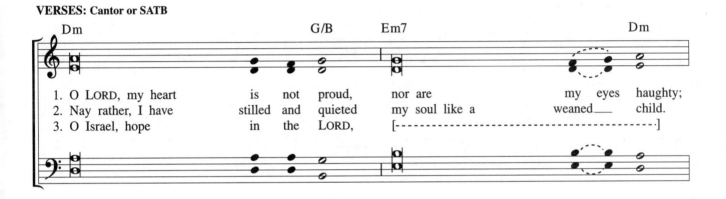

1. O LORD, my heart is not proud, nor are my eyes haughty;
2. Nay rather, I have stilled and quieted my soul like a weaned____ child.
3. O Israel, hope in the LORD, [--]

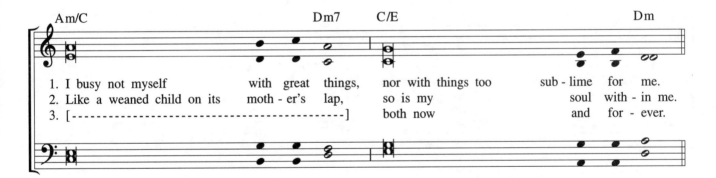

1. I busy not myself with great things, nor with things too sub - lime for me.
2. Like a weaned child on its moth - er's lap, so is my soul with - in me.
3. [--] both now and for - ever.

Gospel Acclamation for this celebration may be found on page 241.
A separate assembly response may be found on page 267.

31ST SUNDAY IN ORDINARY TIME — B

Psalm 18: 2–3, 3–4, 47, 51 [152]

RESPONSE: Cantor/All (♩ = *ca. 80*)

I love you, I love you, Lord, my strength.

VERSES: Cantor or SATB

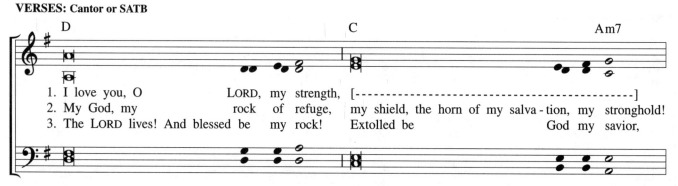

1. I love you, O LORD, my strength, [---]
2. My God, my rock of refuge, my shield, the horn of my salva - tion, my stronghold!
3. The LORD lives! And blessed be my rock! Extolled be God my savior,

1. [---] O LORD, my rock, my fortress, my de - liverer.
2. Praised be the LORD, I ex - claim, and I am safe from my enemies.
3. you who gave great victories to your king and showed kindness to your a - nointed.

Gospel Acclamation for this celebration may be found on page 247.
A separate assembly response may be found on page 265.

31ST SUNDAY IN ORDINARY TIME — C

Psalm 145: 1–2, 8–9, 10–11, 13–14 [153]

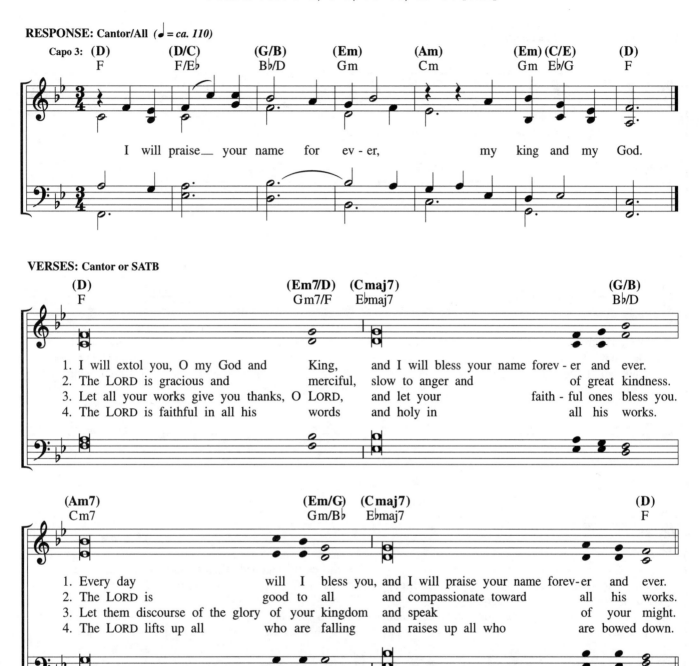

Gospel Acclamation for this celebration may be found on page 253.
A separate assembly response may be found on page 266.

32ND SUNDAY IN ORDINARY TIME — A

Psalm 63: 2, 3–4, 5–6, 7–8 [154]

RESPONSE: Cantor/All (♩ = ca. 42)

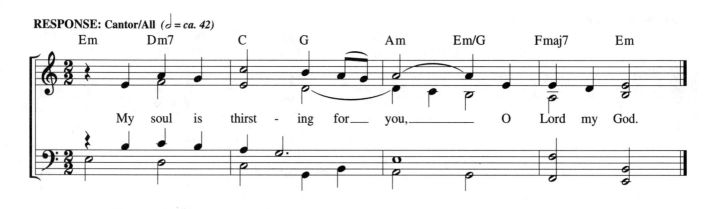

My soul is thirst - ing for___ you,_____ O Lord my God.

VERSES: Cantor or SATB

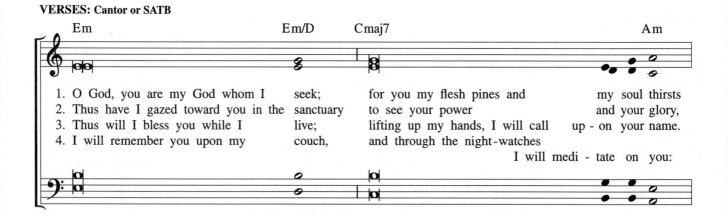

1. O God, you are my God whom I   seek;   for you my flesh pines and   my soul thirsts
2. Thus have I gazed toward you in the   sanctuary   to see your power   and your glory,
3. Thus will I bless you while I   live;   lifting up my hands, I will call   up - on your name.
4. I will remember you upon my   couch,   and through the night-watches

    I will medi - tate on you:

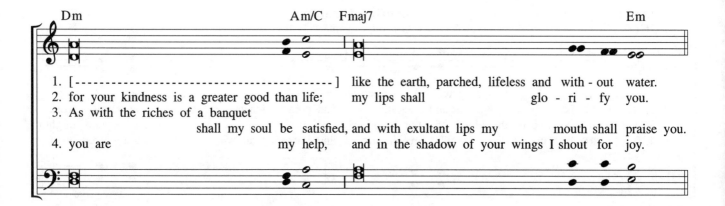

1. [---]   like the earth, parched, lifeless and with - out water.
2. for your kindness is a greater good than life;   my lips shall   glo - ri - fy you.
3. As with the riches of a banquet

    shall my soul be satisfied, and with exultant lips my   mouth shall praise you.
4. you are   my help,   and in the shadow of your wings I shout for joy.

Gospel Acclamation for this celebration may be found on page 241.
A separate assembly response may be found on page 270.

32ND SUNDAY IN ORDINARY TIME — B

Psalm 146: 7, 8–9, 9–10 [155]

RESPONSE: Cantor/All (♩ = ca. 70) [or: Alleluia.]

Praise the Lord, my soul, my soul!

VERSES: Cantor or SATB

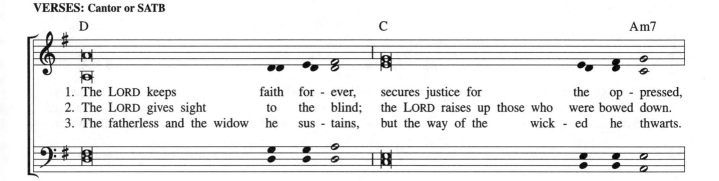

1. The LORD keeps faith for - ever, secures justice for the op - pressed,
2. The LORD gives sight to the blind; the LORD raises up those who were bowed down.
3. The fatherless and the widow he sus - tains, but the way of the wick - ed he thwarts.

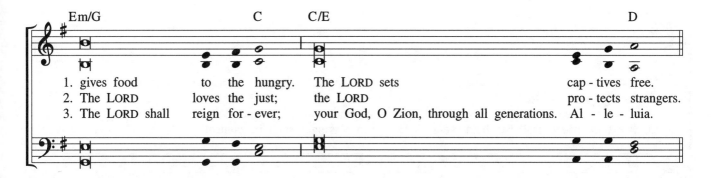

1. gives food to the hungry. The LORD sets cap - tives free.
2. The LORD loves the just; the LORD pro - tects strangers.
3. The LORD shall reign for - ever; your God, O Zion, through all generations. Al - le - luia.

Gospel Acclamation for this celebration may be found on page 247.
A separate assembly response may be found on page 272.

32ND SUNDAY IN ORDINARY TIME — C

Psalm 17: 1, 5–6, 8, 15 [156]

RESPONSE: Cantor/All (♩. = *ca. 55*)

Lord,___ when your glo - ry ap - pears,___ my joy will be full._____

VERSES: Cantor or SATB

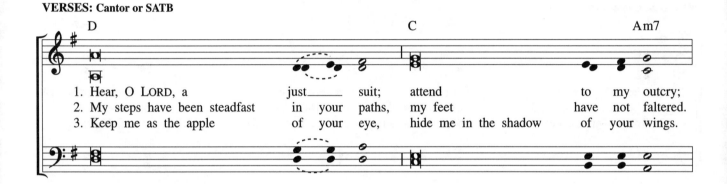

1. Hear, O LORD, a just____ suit; attend to my outcry;
2. My steps have been steadfast in your paths, my feet have not faltered.
3. Keep me as the apple of your eye, hide me in the shadow of your wings.

1. [--] hearken to my prayer from lips with-out de-ceit.
2. I call upon you, for you will answer me, O God; incline your ear to me; hear my word.
3. But I in justice shall be-hold your face; on waking I shall be content in your presence.

Gospel Acclamation for this celebration may be found on page 253.
A separate assembly response may be found on page 270.

33rd Sunday in Ordinary Time — A

Psalm 128: 1–2, 3, 4–5 [157]

Gospel Acclamation for this celebration may be found on page 241.
A separate assembly response may be found on page 262.

33RD SUNDAY IN ORDINARY TIME — B

Psalm 16: 5, 8, 9–10, 11 [158]

RESPONSE: Cantor/All (♩ = ca. 95)

You are my in - her - i - tance, O Lord!

VERSES: Cantor or SATB

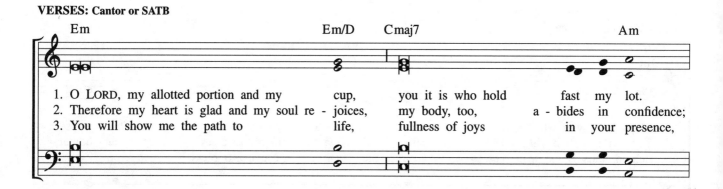

1. O LORD, my allotted portion and my cup, you it is who hold fast my lot.
2. Therefore my heart is glad and my soul re - joices, my body, too, a - bides in confidence;
3. You will show me the path to life, fullness of joys in your presence,

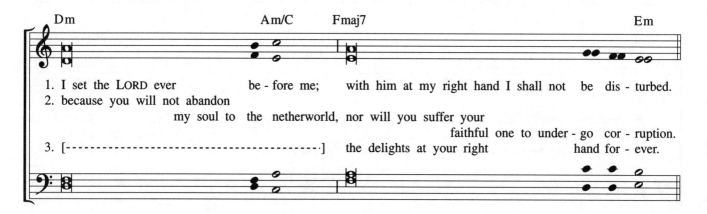

1. I set the LORD ever be - fore me; with him at my right hand I shall not be dis - turbed.
2. because you will not abandon my soul to the netherworld, nor will you suffer your faithful one to under - go cor - ruption.
3. [---] the delights at your right hand for - ever.

Gospel Acclamation for this celebration may be found on page 247.
A separate assembly response may be found on page 277.

33RD SUNDAY IN ORDINARY TIME — C

Psalm 98: 5–6, 7–8, 9 [159]

RESPONSE: Cantor/All (♩ = *ca. 90*)

The Lord comes to rule the earth with jus - tice.

VERSES: Cantor or SATB

1. Sing praise to the LORD with the harp, with the harp and me - lo - dious song.
2. Let the sea and what fills it re - sound, the world and those who dwell in it;
3. Before the LORD, for he comes, for he comes to rule the earth;

1. With trumpets and the sound of the horn sing joyfully before the King, the LORD.
2. let the rivers clap their hands, the mountains shout with them for joy.
3. he will rule the world with justice and the peo - ples with equity.

Gospel Acclamation for this celebration may be found on page 253.
A separate assembly response may be found on page 273.

OUR LORD JESUS CHRIST THE KING — A

Psalm 23: 1–2, 2–3, 5–6 [160]

Gospel Acclamation for this celebration may be found on page 235.
A separate assembly response may be found on page 274.

OUR LORD JESUS CHRIST THE KING — B

Psalm 93: 1, 1–2, 5 [161]

RESPONSE (♩ = ca. 75)

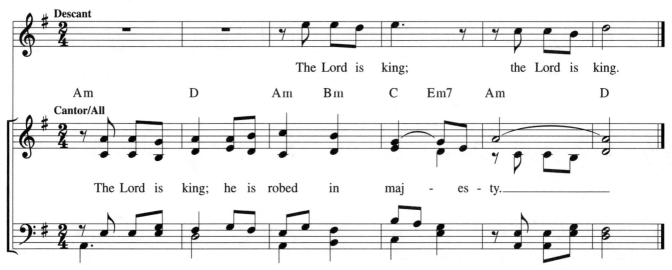

Descant

The Lord is king; the Lord is king.

Cantor/All

The Lord is king; he is robed in maj - es - ty.

VERSES: Cantor or SATB

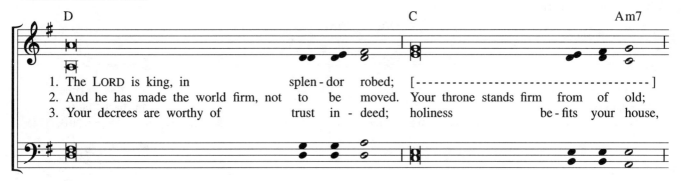

1. The LORD is king, in splen - dor robed; [- -]
2. And he has made the world firm, not to be moved. Your throne stands firm from of old;
3. Your decrees are worthy of trust in - deed; holiness be - fits your house,

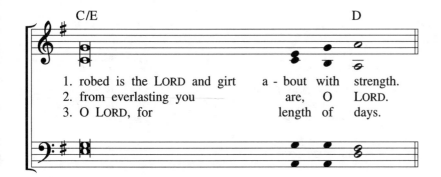

1. robed is the LORD and girt a - bout with strength.
2. from everlasting you are, O LORD.
3. O LORD, for length of days.

Gospel Acclamation for this celebration may be found on page 235.
A separate assembly response may be found on page 274.

OUR LORD JESUS CHRIST THE KING — C

Psalm 122: 1–2, 3–4, 4–5 [162]

RESPONSE (♩ = ca. 80)

Descant

Let us go re-joic - ing, re-joic - ing let us go.

Cantor/All

Let us go re-joic - ing to the house of the Lord.

VERSES: Cantor or SATB

1. I rejoiced because they said to me, "We will go up to the house of the LORD."
2. Jerusalem, built as a city with com-pact unity.
3. According to the de-cree for Israel, to give thanks to the name of the LORD.

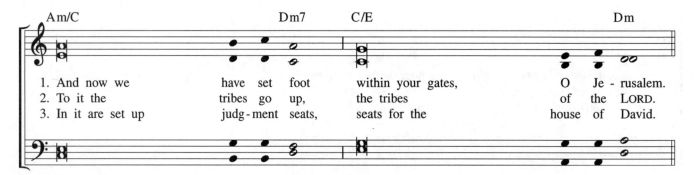

1. And now we have set foot within your gates, O Je-rusalem.
2. To it the tribes go up, the tribes of the LORD.
3. In it are set up judg-ment seats, seats for the house of David.

Gospel Acclamation for this celebration may be found on page 235.
A separate assembly response may be found on page 267.

THANKSGIVING DAY

Psalm 113: 1–2, 3–4, 5–6, 7–8 [945–2]

RESPONSE: Cantor/All (♩ = ca. 80) [*or:* Alleluia.]

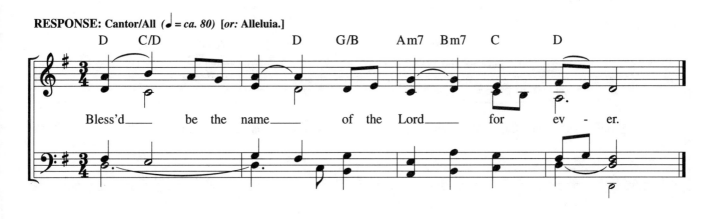

Bless'd____ be the name____ of the Lord____ for ev - er.

VERSES: Cantor or SATB

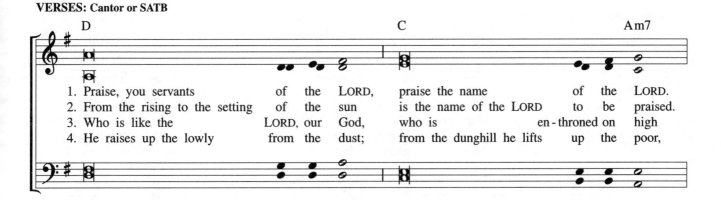

1. Praise, you servants of the LORD, praise the name of the LORD.
2. From the rising to the setting of the sun is the name of the LORD to be praised.
3. Who is like the LORD, our God, who is en-throned on high
4. He raises up the lowly from the dust; from the dunghill he lifts up the poor,

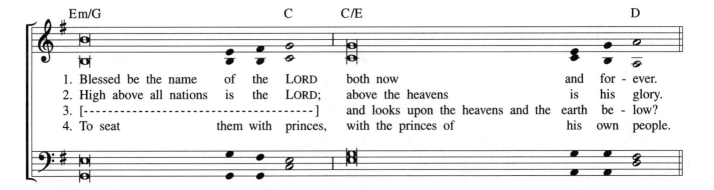

1. Blessed be the name of the LORD both now and for - ever.
2. High above all nations is the LORD; above the heavens is his glory.
3. [-------------------------------------] and looks upon the heavens and the earth be - low?
4. To seat them with princes, with the princes of his own people.

Gospel Acclamation for this celebration may be found on page 259.
A separate assembly response may be found on page 263.

FEBRUARY 2 — PRESENTATION OF THE LORD

Psalm 24: 7, 8, 9, 10 [524]

RESPONSE: Cantor/All (♩ = *ca. 80*)

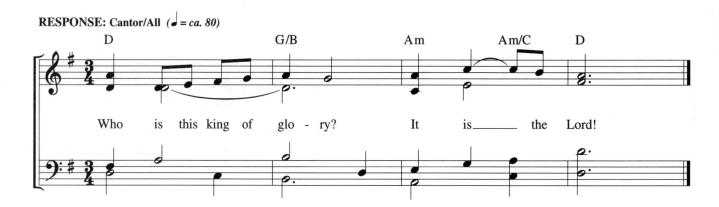

Who is this king of glo - ry? It is____ the Lord!

VERSES: Cantor or SATB

1. Lift up, O   gates, your lintels; reach up, you   an - cient portals,
2. Who is this   king of glory? The LORD,   strong and mighty,
3. Lift up, O   gates, your lintels; reach up, you   an - cient portals,
4. Who is this   king of glory? [---]

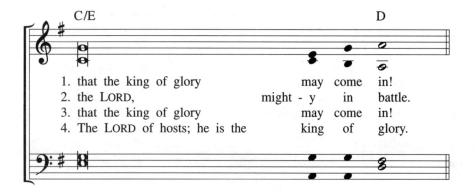

1. that the king of glory   may come in!
2. the LORD,   might - y in battle.
3. that the king of glory   may come in!
4. The LORD of hosts; he is the   king of glory.

Gospel Acclamation for this celebration may be found on page 254.
A separate assembly response may be found on page 277.

MARCH 19 — ST. JOSEPH, HUSBAND OF THE VIRGIN MARY

Psalm 89: 2–3, 4–5, 27 and 29 [543]

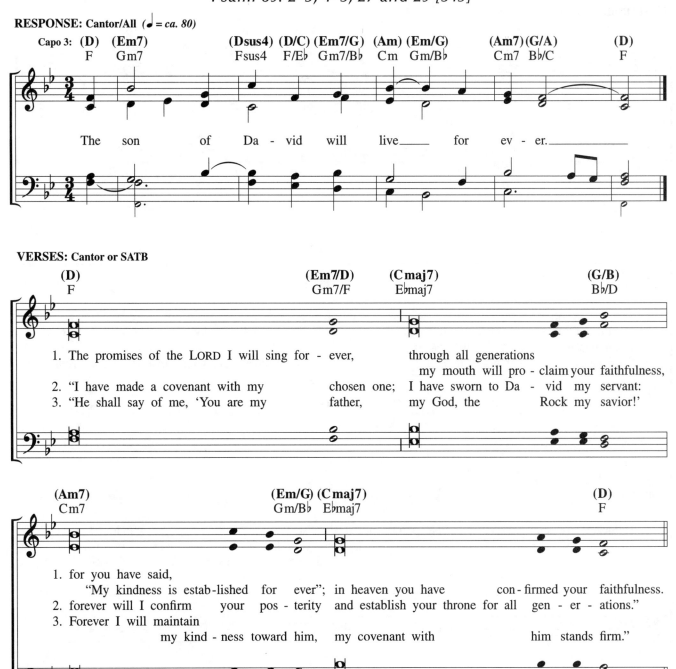

Gospel Acclamation for this celebration may be found on page 254 or 255.
A separate assembly response may be found on page 275.

MARCH 25 — ANNUNCIATION OF THE LORD

Psalm 40: 7–8, 8–9, 10, 11 [545]

RESPONSE: Cantor/All (♩ = *ca. 90*)

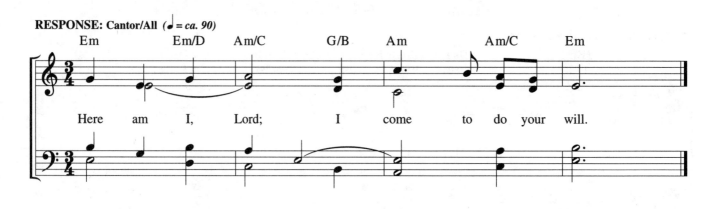

Here am I, Lord; I come to do your will.

VERSES: Cantor or SATB

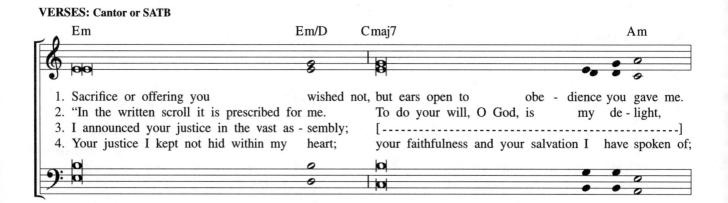

1. Sacrifice or offering you wished not, but ears open to obe - dience you gave me.
2. "In the written scroll it is prescribed for me. To do your will, O God, is my de - light,
3. I announced your justice in the vast as - sembly; [-----------------------------------]
4. Your justice I kept not hid within my heart; your faithfulness and your salvation I have spoken of;

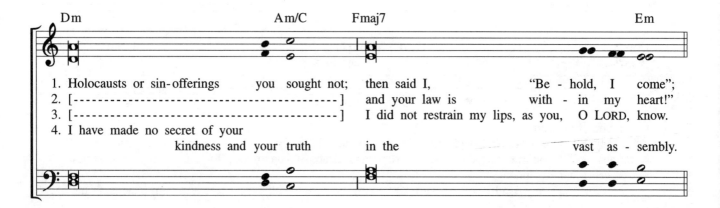

1. Holocausts or sin-offerings you sought not; then said I, "Be - hold, I come";
2. [--] and your law is with - in my heart!"
3. [--] I did not restrain my lips, as you, O LORD, know.
4. I have made no secret of your kindness and your truth in the vast as - sembly.

Gospel Acclamation for this celebration may be found on page 254 or 255.
A separate assembly response may be found on page 265.

JUNE 23 — NATIVITY OF ST. JOHN THE BAPTIST: VIGIL MASS

Psalm 71: 1–2, 3–4a, 5–6ab, 15ab and 17 [586]

RESPONSE: Cantor/All (♩ = *ca. 75*)

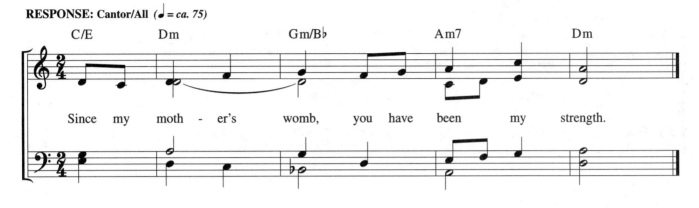

Since my moth-er's womb, you have been my strength.

VERSES: Cantor or SATB

1. In you, O LORD, I take refuge; let me never be put to shame.
2. Be my rock of refuge, a stonghold to give me safety,
3. For you are my hope, O Lord; my trust, O God, from my youth.
4. My mouth shall de-clare your justice, day by day your sal - vation.

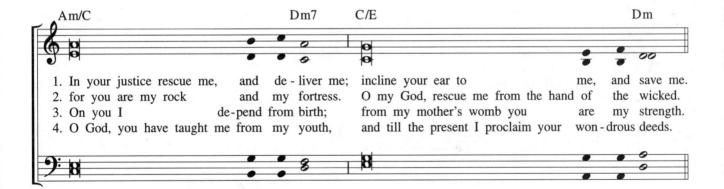

1. In your justice rescue me, and de - liver me; incline your ear to me, and save me.
2. for you are my rock and my fortress. O my God, rescue me from the hand of the wicked.
3. On you I de-pend from birth; from my mother's womb you are my strength.
4. O God, you have taught me from my youth, and till the present I proclaim your won - drous deeds.

Gospel Acclamation for this celebration may be found on page 254.
A separate assembly response may be found on page 272.

JUNE 24 — NATIVITY OF ST. JOHN THE BAPTIST

Psalm 139: 1–3, 13–14ab, 14c–15 [587]

RESPONSE: Cantor/All (♩ = *ca. 70*)

I praise you for I am won-der-ful-ly made.

VERSES: Cantor or SATB

1. O LORD, you have probed me and you know me; you know when I sit and when I stand; you understand my thoughts from a-far.
2. Truly you have formed my in-most being; you knit me in my moth-er's womb.
3. My soul also you knew full well; nor was my frame un-known to you

1. My journeys and my rest you scrutinize, with all my ways you are fa-miliar.
2. I give you thanks that I am fearfully, wonder-ful-ly made; wonderful are your works.
3. when I was made in secret, when I was fashioned in the depths of the earth.

Gospel Acclamation for this celebration may be found on page 254.
A separate assembly response may be found on page 265.

JUNE 28 — SAINTS PETER AND PAUL, APOSTLES: VIGIL MASS

Psalm 19: 2–3, 4–5 [590]

RESPONSE: Cantor/All (♩ = *ca. 85*)

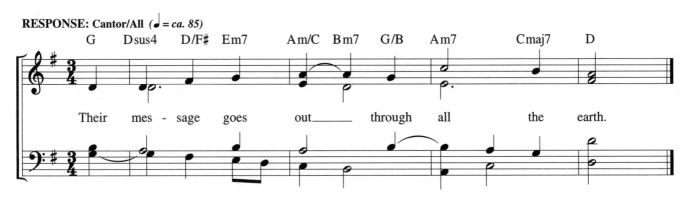

Their mes-sage goes out____ through all the earth.

VERSES: Cantor or SATB

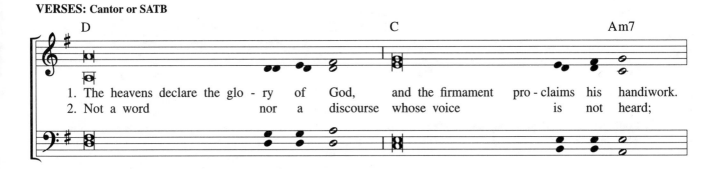

1. The heavens declare the glo-ry of God, and the firmament pro-claims his handiwork.
2. Not a word nor a discourse whose voice is not heard;

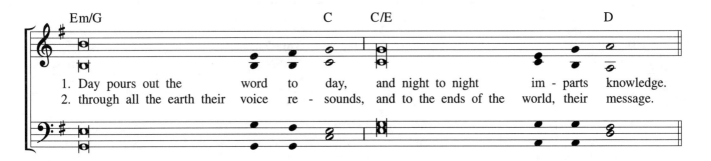

1. Day pours out the word to day, and night to night im-parts knowledge.
2. through all the earth their voice re-sounds, and to the ends of the world, their message.

Gospel Acclamation for this celebration may be found on page 256.
A separate assembly response may be found on page 276.

JUNE 29 — SAINTS PETER AND PAUL, APOSTLES

Psalm 34: 2–3, 4–5, 6–7, 8–9 [591]

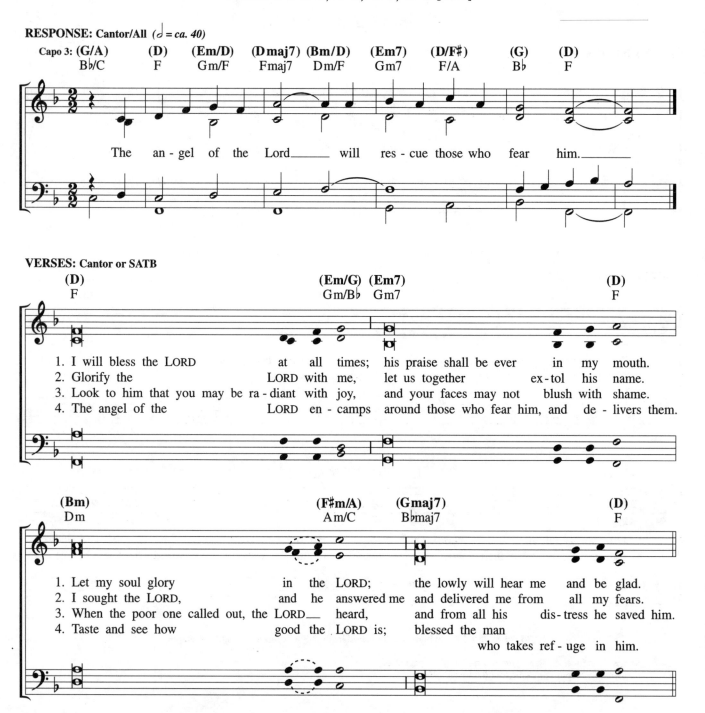

RESPONSE: Cantor/All (♩ = ca. 40)

The an-gel of the Lord will res-cue those who fear him.

VERSES: Cantor or SATB

1. I will bless the LORD at all times; his praise shall be ever in my mouth.
2. Glorify the LORD with me, let us together ex-tol his name.
3. Look to him that you may be ra-diant with joy, and your faces may not blush with shame.
4. The angel of the LORD en-camps around those who fear him, and de-livers them.

1. Let my soul glory in the LORD; the lowly will hear me and be glad.
2. I sought the LORD, and he answered me and delivered me from all my fears.
3. When the poor one called out, the LORD heard, and from all his dis-tress he saved him.
4. Taste and see how good the LORD is; blessed the man who takes ref-uge in him.

Gospel Acclamation for this celebration may be found on page 256.
A separate assembly response may be found on page 273.

AUGUST 6 — TRANSFIGURATION OF THE LORD

Psalm 97: 1–2, 5–6, 9 [614]

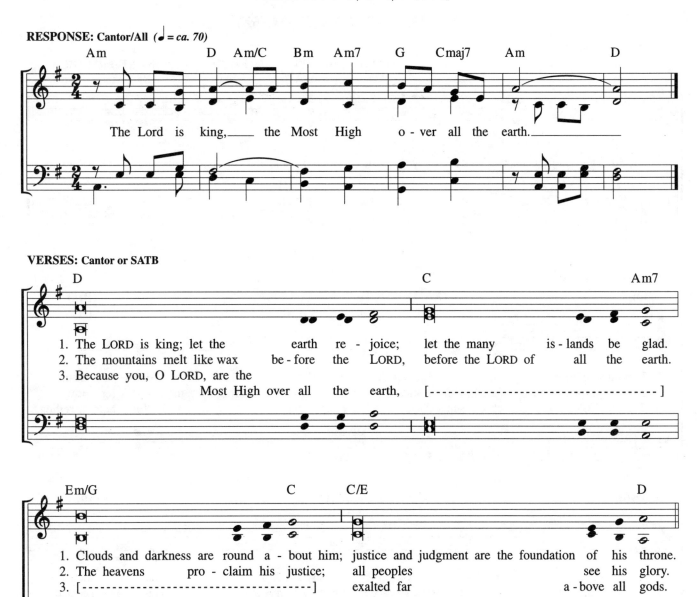

Gospel Acclamation for this celebration may be found on page 256.
A separate assembly response may be found on page 274.

AUGUST 14 — ASSUMPTION OF
THE BLESSED VIRGIN MARY: VIGIL MASS

Psalm 132: 6–7, 9–10, 13–14 [621]

Gospel Acclamation for this celebration may be found on page 256.
A separate assembly response may be found on page 268.

August 15 — Assumption of the Blessed Virgin Mary

Psalm 45: 10, 11, 12, 16 [622]

RESPONSE: Cantor/All (♩ = *ca. 50*)

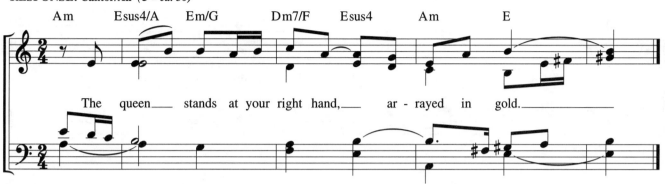

The queen stands at your right hand, ar-rayed in gold.

VERSES: Cantor or SATB

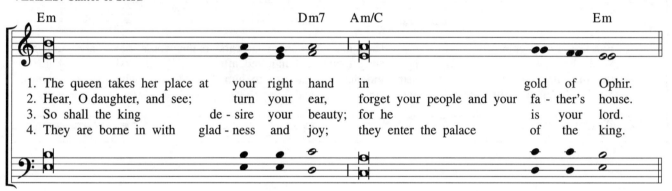

1. The queen takes her place at your right hand in gold of Ophir.
2. Hear, O daughter, and see; turn your ear, forget your people and your fa-ther's house.
3. So shall the king de-sire your beauty; for he is your lord.
4. They are borne in with glad-ness and joy; they enter the palace of the king.

Gospel Acclamation for this celebration may be found on page 256.
A separate assembly response may be found on page 275.

SEPTEMBER 14 — EXALTATION OF THE HOLY CROSS

Psalm 78: 1–2, 34–35, 36–37, 38 [638]

RESPONSE: Cantor/All (♩ = *ca. 90*)

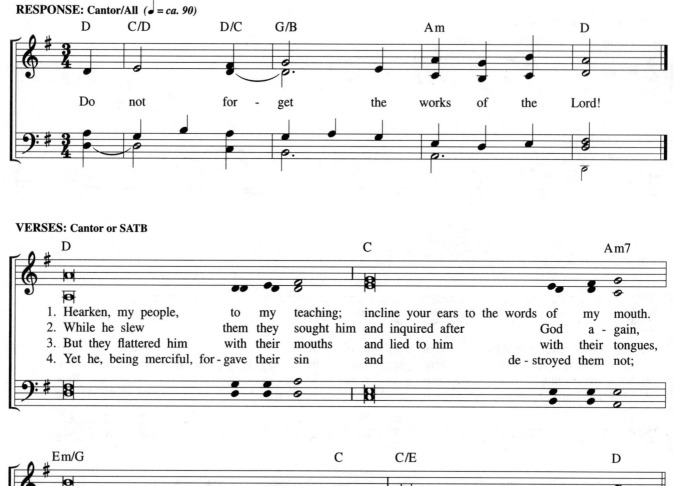

Do not for-get the works of the Lord!

VERSES: Cantor or SATB

1. Hearken, my people, to my teaching; incline your ears to the words of my mouth.
2. While he slew them they sought him and inquired after God a-gain,
3. But they flattered him with their mouths and lied to him with their tongues,
4. Yet he, being merciful, for-gave their sin and de-stroyed them not;

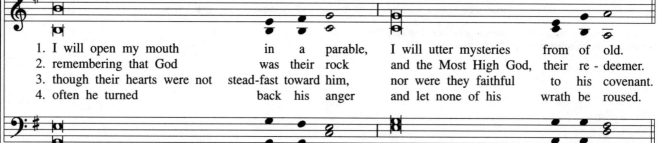

1. I will open my mouth in a parable, I will utter mysteries from of old.
2. remembering that God was their rock and the Most High God, their re-deemer.
3. though their hearts were not stead-fast toward him, nor were they faithful to his covenant.
4. often he turned back his anger and let none of his wrath be roused.

Gospel Acclamation for this celebration may be found on page 256.
A separate assembly response may be found on page 263.

Psalm 24: 1–2, 3–4ab, 5–6 [667]

RESPONSE (♩. = *ca. 40*)

Descant

Lord,__ this is the peo-ple that__ longs to__ see your face.

Cantor/All

Lord,__ this is the peo-ple that longs to see your face.

VERSES: Cantor or SATB

1. The LORD's are the earth and its fullness; the world and those who dwell in it.
2. Who can ascend the mountain of the LORD? or who may stand in his ho - ly place?
3. He shall receive a blessing from the LORD, a reward from God his savior.

1. For he founded it up - on the seas and established it up - on the rivers.
2. One whose hands are sinless, whose heart is clean, who desires not what is vain.
3. Such is the race that seeks for him, that seeks the face of the God of Jacob.

Gospel Acclamation for this celebration may be found on page 257.
A separate assembly response may be found on page 270.

November 2 — Commemoration of All the Faithful Departed (All Souls)

Psalm 23: 1–3a, 3b–4, 5, 6 [668–1]

Gospel Acclamation for this celebration may be found on page 257.
Separate assembly responses may be found on pages 274 and 276.

NOVEMBER 2 — COMMEMORATION OF ALL THE FAITHFUL DEPARTED (All Souls)

Psalm 25: 6 and 7b, 17–18, 20–21 [668–2]

Gospel Acclamation for this celebration may be found on page 257.
Separate assembly responses may be found on pages 276 and 271.

NOVEMBER 2 — COMMEMORATION OF ALL THE FAITHFUL DEPARTED (All Souls)

Psalm 27: 1, 4, 7 and 8b and 9a, 13–14 [668–3]

OR

RESPONSE: Cantor/All (♩ = ca. 45)

The Lord is my light and my sal-va-tion.

OR (♩ = ca. 70)

I be-lieve that I shall see the good things of the Lord in the land of the liv - ing.

VERSES: Cantor or SATB

1. The LORD is my light and my sal - vation; whom should I fear?
2. One thing I ask of the LORD; this I seek: to dwell in the house of the LORD all the days of my life,
3. Hear, O LORD, the sound of my call; have pity on me and answer me.
4. I believe that I shall see the bounty of the LORD in the land of the living.

1. The LORD is my life's refuge; of whom should I be a - fraid?
2. that I may gaze on the loveliness of the LORD and contem - plate his temple.
3. Your presence, O LORD, I seek! Hide not your face from me.
4. Wait for the LORD with courage; be stouthearted and wait for the LORD!

Gospel Acclamation for this celebration may be found on page 257.
Separate assembly responses may be found on pages 274 and 265.

210

November 3 — Saint Martin de Porres

Psalm 131: 1bcde, 2, 3 [669]

RESPONSE: Cantor/All (♩ = *ca. 80*)

In you, Lord, I have found my peace, I have found my peace.

VERSES: Cantor or SATB

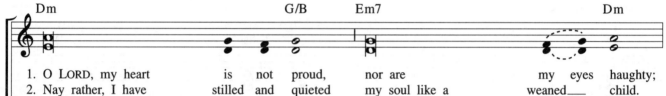

1. O LORD, my heart is not proud, nor are my eyes haughty;
2. Nay rather, I have stilled and quieted my soul like a weaned child.
3. O Israel, hope in the LORD, [--]

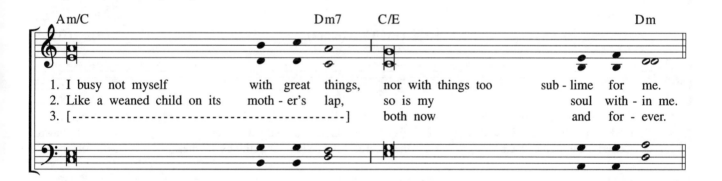

1. I busy not myself with great things, nor with things too sub-lime for me.
2. Like a weaned child on its moth-er's lap, so is my soul with-in me.
3. [--] both now and for-ever.

Gospel Acclamation for this celebration may be found on page 258.
A separate assembly response may be found on page 267.

November 9 — Dedication of the Lateran Basilica in Rome

Psalm 46: 2–3, 5–6, 8–9 [671]

Gospel Acclamation for this celebration may be found on page 258.
A separate assembly response may be found on page 276.

December 8 — Immaculate Conception of the Blessed Virgin Mary

Psalm 98: 1, 2–3, 3–4 [689]

RESPONSE: Cantor/All (♩. = *ca. 40*)

Sing to the Lord a new song, ___ for he has done mar - vel-ous deeds. ___

VERSES: Cantor or SATB

1. Sing to the LORD a new song, for he has done won-drous deeds;
2. The LORD has made his salvation known: in the sight of the nations he has re - vealed his justice.
3. All the ends of the earth have seen the salvation by our God.

1. His right hand has won vic - t'ry for him, his ho - ly arm.
2. He has remembered his kindness and his faithfulness toward the house of Israel.
3. Sing joyfully to the LORD, all you lands; break into song; sing praise.

Gospel Acclamation for this celebration may be found on page 258.
A separate assembly response may be found on page 272.

DECEMBER 12 — OUR LADY OF GUADALUPE

Judith 13: 18bcde, 19 [690A]

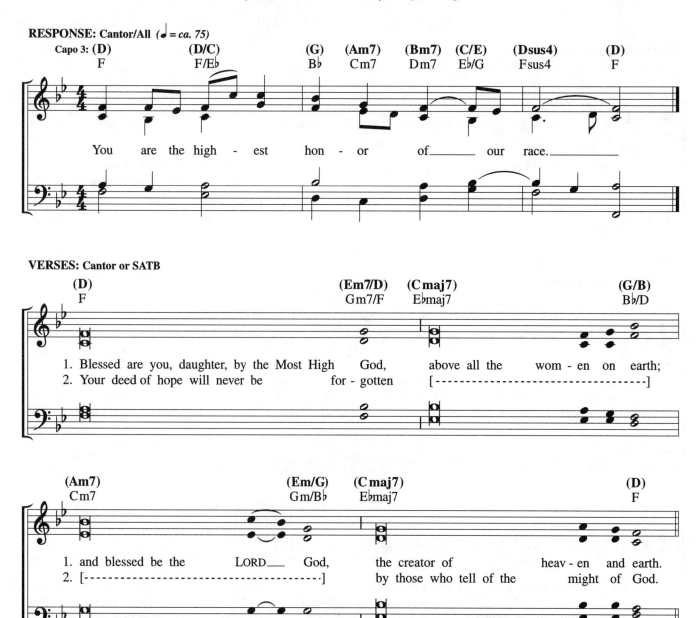

Gospel Acclamation for this celebration may be found on page 258.
A separate assembly response may be found on page 277.

COMMON PSALM FOR THE SEASON OF ADVENT

Psalm 85: 9ab and 10, 11–12, 13–14 [174–2]

RESPONSE: Cantor/All (♩ = *ca. 70*)

Lord,__ Lord,__ show us your mer-cy and love,__ your mer-cy and love.

VERSES: Cantor or SATB

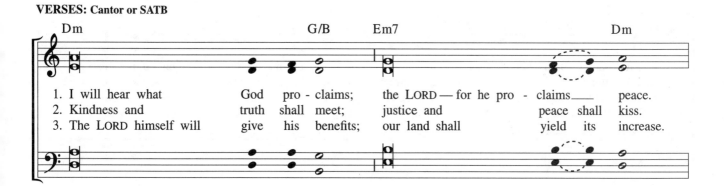

1. I will hear what God pro-claims; the LORD—for he pro-claims__ peace.
2. Kindness and truth shall meet; justice and peace shall kiss.
3. The LORD himself will give his benefits; our land shall yield its increase.

1. Near indeed is his salvation to those who fear him, glory dwelling in our land.
2. Truth shall spring out of the earth, and justice shall look down from heaven.
3. Justice shall walk be-fore him, and prepare the way of his steps.

A separate assembly response may be found on page 269.

COMMON PSALM FOR EASTER VIGIL

Psalm 136: 1–3, 4–6, 7–9, 24–26 [174–9a]

A separate assembly response may be found on page 265.

COMMON PSALM FOR EASTER VIGIL

Psalm 136: 1, 3, 16, 21–23, 24–26 [174–9b]

A separate assembly response may be found on page 265.

COMMON PSALM FOR THE SEASON OF EASTER

Psalm 66: 1–3, 4–5, 6–7, 16, 20 [174–11]

RESPONSE: Cantor/All (♩ = ca. 65)

Let all the earth___ cry out to God with joy, al - le - lu - ia.

VERSES: Cantor or SATB

1. Shout joyfully to God, all the earth; sing praise to the glory of his name;
2. "Let all on earth worship and sing praise to you, sing praise to your name!"
3. He has changed the sea in - to dry land; through the river they passed on foot;
4. Hear now, all you who fear God, while I declare what he has done for me.

1. proclaim his glo-rious praise. Say to God, "How tremendous are your deeds!"
2. Come and see the works of God, his tremendous deeds among the chil - dren of Adam.
3. therefore let us re - joice in him, he rules by his might for - ever.
4. Blessed be God, who re - fused me not my prayer or his kindness!

A separate assembly response may be found on page 267.

COMMON PSALM FOR ASCENSION

Psalm 47: 2–3, 6–7, 8–9 [174–12]

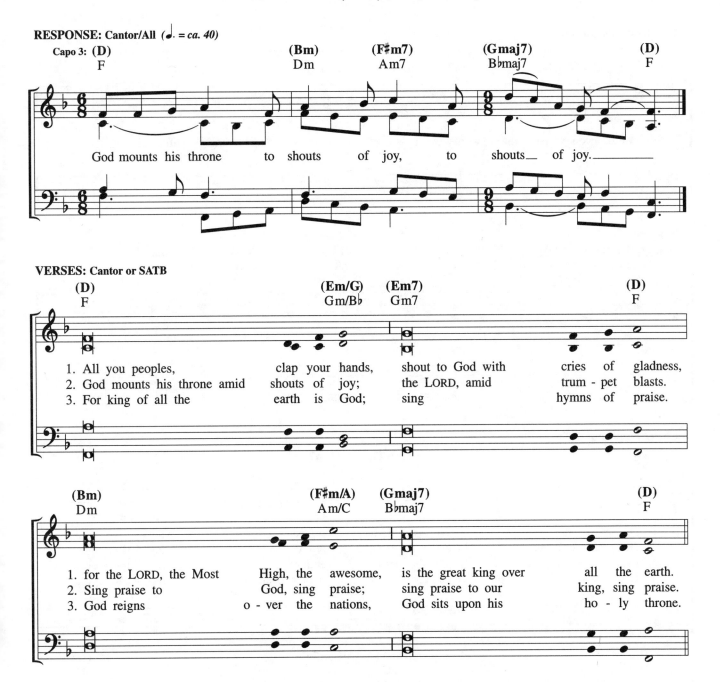

A separate assembly response may be found on page 264.

COMMON PSALM FOR ORDINARY TIME

Psalm 19: 8, 9, 10, 11 [174–14]

Separate assembly responses may be found on pages 270 and 278.

COMMON PSALM FOR ORDINARY TIME

Psalm 34: 2–3, 4–5, 6–7, 8–9 [174–16]

Separate assembly responses may be found on pages 266 and 272.

RITE OF ENTRANCE INTO THE ORDER OF CATECHUMENS

Psalm 33: 4–5, 12–13, 18–19, 20 and 22 [743]

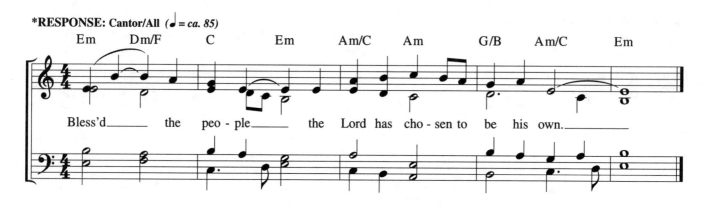

*RESPONSE: Cantor/All (♩ = *ca. 85*)

Bless'd_____ the peo-ple_____ the Lord has cho-sen to be his own._____

VERSES: Cantor or SATB

1. For upright is the word of the LORD, and all his works are trustworthy.
2. Blessed the nation whose God is the LORD, the people he has chosen for his own in-heritance.
3. But see, the eyes of the LORD are upon those who fear him, upon those who hope for his kindness,
4. Our soul waits for the LORD, who is our help and our shield.

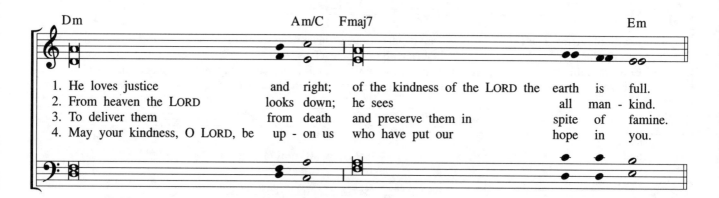

1. He loves justice and right; of the kindness of the LORD the earth is full.
2. From heaven the LORD looks down; he sees all man-kind.
3. To deliver them from death and preserve them in spite of famine.
4. May your kindness, O LORD, be up-on us who have put our hope in you.

*Alternate response: "Lord, let your mercy be on us, as we place our trust in you."

Gospel Acclamation for this celebration may be found on page 259 or 260.
A separate assembly response may be found on page 263.

GOSPEL ACCLAMATIONS

ADVENT ABC
Sundays 1–4

ACCLAMATION: All (♩ = *ca. 75*)

Al - le - lu - ia, al - le - lu - ia, al - le - lu - ia.

VERSE: Cantor or SATB

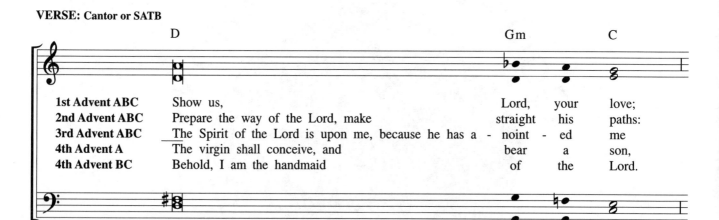

1st Advent ABC	Show us, ... Lord, your love;
2nd Advent ABC	Prepare the way of the Lord, make ... straight his paths:
3rd Advent ABC	The Spirit of the Lord is upon me, because he has a - noint - ed me
4th Advent A	The virgin shall conceive, and ... bear a son,
4th Advent BC	Behold, I am the handmaid ... of the Lord.

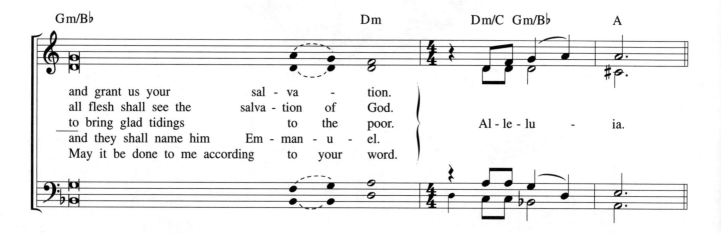

and grant us your sal - va - tion.
all flesh shall see the salva - tion of God.
to bring glad tidings to the poor.   Al - le - lu - ia.
and they shall name him Em - man - u - el.
May it be done to me according to your word.

A separate assembly response may be found on page 278.

NATIVITY OF THE LORD (Christmas) ABC
Vigil, Midnight, Dawn and Day

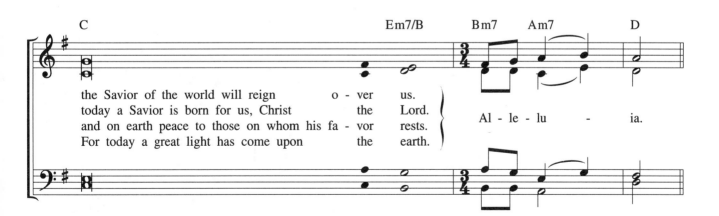

A separate assembly response may be found on page 278.

Holy Family ABC, Mary, the Mother of God ABC and Second Sunday after Christmas ABC

ACCLAMATION (♩ = ca. 95)

Descant

Al - le - lu - ia, _____ al - le - lu - ia, al - le - lu - ia. _____

All

Al - le - lu - ia, al - le - lu - ia, al - le - lu - ia.

VERSE: Cantor or SATB

Holy Family ABC	Let the peace of Christ	con - trol	your	hearts;
Holy Family B (Optional)	In the past God spoke to our ancestors	through	the	prophets;
Holy Family C (Optional)	Open our	hearts,	O	Lord,
Mary, Mother of God ABC	In the past God spoke to our ancestors	through	the	prophets;
2nd Sunday after Christmas ABC	Glory to you, O Christ, proclaimed	to	the	Gentiles;

let the word of Christ dwell in you richly.
in these last days, he has spoken to us through the Son.
to listen to the words of your Son. Al - le - lu - ia.
in these last days, he has spoken to us through the Son.
Glory to you, O Christ, believed in throughout the world!

A separate assembly response may be found on page 278.

EPIPHANY ABC AND BAPTISM OF THE LORD ABC

ACCLAMATION (♩ = ca. 95)

VERSE: Cantor or SATB

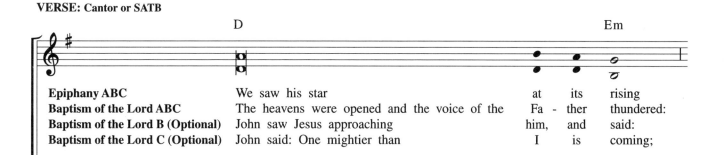

Epiphany ABC	We saw his star at its rising
Baptism of the Lord ABC	The heavens were opened and the voice of the Fa - ther thundered:
Baptism of the Lord B (Optional)	John saw Jesus approaching him, and said:
Baptism of the Lord C (Optional)	John said: One mightier than I is coming;

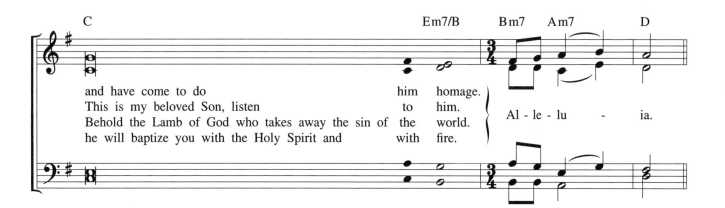

and have come to do him homage.
This is my beloved Son, listen to him.
Behold the Lamb of God who takes away the sin of the world.
he will baptize you with the Holy Spirit and with fire.

Al - le - lu - ia.

A separate assembly response may be found on page 278.

ASH WEDNESDAY AND LENT ABC
Sundays 1–2

A separate assembly response may be found on page 278.

LENT ABC
Sundays 3–4

ACCLAMATION: All (♩ = ca. 60)

Praise to you, Lord Je - sus Christ, King of end - less glo - ry!

OR

ACCLAMATION: All (♩ = ca. 85)

Glo - ry to you, Word of God, Lord Je - sus Christ!_____

VERSE: Cantor or SATB

3rd Lent A	Lord, you are truly the Savior of the world;
3rd Lent B	God so loved the world that he gave his on - ly Son,
3rd Lent C	___Repent, says the Lord;
4th Lent A	I am the light of the world, says the Lord;
4th Lent B	God so loved the world that he gave his on - ly Son,
4th Lent C	I will get up and go to my Father and shall say to him:

give me living water, that I may never thirst a - gain.
so that everyone who believes in him might have e - ter - nal life.
the kingdom of heaven is at hand.
whoever follows me will have the light of life.
so everyone who believes in him might have e - ter - nal life.
Father, I have sinned against heaven and a - gainst_____ you.

A separate assembly response may be found on page 278.

FIFTH SUNDAY OF LENT ABC, PALM SUNDAY ABC, HOLY THURSDAY ABC AND GOOD FRIDAY ABC

A separate assembly response may be found on page 278.

VERSE: Cantor or SATB

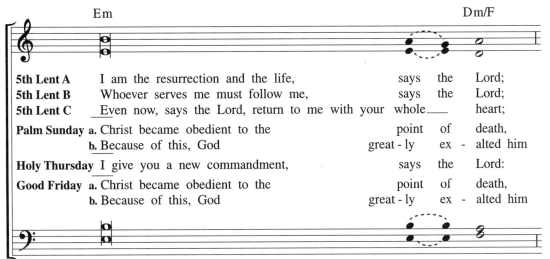

5th Lent A	I am the resurrection and the life, says the Lord;
5th Lent B	Whoever serves me must follow me, says the Lord;
5th Lent C	Even now, says the Lord, return to me with your whole____ heart;
Palm Sunday a.	Christ became obedient to the point of death,
b.	Because of this, God great - ly ex - alted him
Holy Thursday	I give you a new commandment, says the Lord:
Good Friday a.	Christ became obedient to the point of death,
b.	Because of this, God great - ly ex - alted him

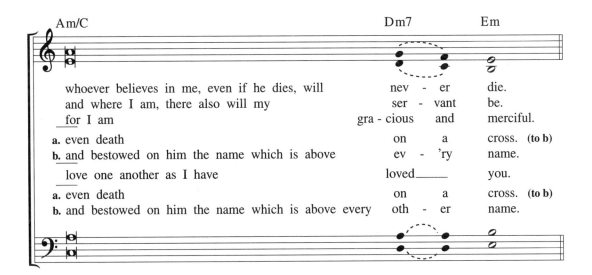

	whoever believes in me, even if he dies, will nev - er die.
	and where I am, there also will my ser - vant be.
	for I am gra - cious and merciful.
a.	even death on a cross. **(to b)**
b.	and bestowed on him the name which is above ev - 'ry name.
	love one another as I have loved____ you.
a.	even death on a cross. **(to b)**
b.	and bestowed on him the name which is above every oth - er name.

EASTER ABC
Easter Sunday and Sundays 2–3

VERSE: Cantor or SATB

Easter Sunday ABC	Christ, our paschal lamb,	has been sacrificed;
2nd Easter ABC	You believe in me, Thomas, because you have seen me,	says the Lord;
3rd Easter AB	Lord Jesus, open the	Scrip - tures to us;
3rd Easter C	Christ is risen,	crea - tor of all;

let us then feast with joy in	the Lord.
blessed are they who have not seen me, but still	be - lieve!
make our hearts burn while you speak	to us.
he has shown pity on	all people.

Al - le - lu - ia.

A separate assembly response may be found on page 278.

EASTER ABC
Sundays 4–5

ACCLAMATION (♩. = *ca. 40*)

Descant

Al - le - lu - ia,   al - le - lu - ia,_____ al - le - lu - ia.

Capo 3: **(D)** **(A)** **(Em)** **(Bm)** **(F♯m)** **(F♯m/A)** **(Em7/G)** **(D)**
F   C   Gm   Dm   Am   Am/C   Gm7/B♭   F

All

Al - le - lu - ia,   al - le - lu - ia,   al - le - lu - ia._____

VERSE: Cantor or SATB

(D) **(A)**
F   C

4th Easter ABC	I am the good shepherd,	says	the	Lord;
5th Easter A	I am the way, the truth and the life,	says	the	Lord;
5th Easter B	Remain in me as I remain in you,	says	the	Lord.
5th Easter C	I give you a new commandment,	says	the	Lord:

(F♯m/A) **(Bm)** **(Em7)** **(A)**
Am/C   Dm   Gm7   C

I know my sheep, and mine   know   me.
no one comes to the Father, except   through   me.
Whoever remains in me will bear   much   fruit.
love one another as I have   loved   you.

Al - le - lu - ia.

A separate assembly response may be found on page 278.

EASTER ABC
Sunday 6, Ascension, Sunday 7 and Pentecost

A separate assembly response may be found on page 278.

SOLEMNITIES OF THE LORD IN ORDINARY TIME ABC
Holy Trinity, Body and Blood, Sacred Heart and Christ the King

ACCLAMATION (♩. = ca. 40)

Descant

Al - le - lu - ia,   al - le - lu - ia,_____   al - le - lu - ia.

Capo 3: (D)   (A)   (Em)   (Bm)   (F♯m)   (F♯m/A)   (Em7/G)   (D)
         F   C   Gm   Dm   Am   Am/C   Gm7/B♭   F

All

Al - le - lu - ia,   al - le - lu - ia,   al - le - lu - ia._____

VERSE: Cantor or SATB   (D)   (A)
                                F   C

Holy Trinity ABC	Glory to the Father, the Son, and the ... Ho - ly Spirit;
Body and Blood ABC	I am the living bread that came down from heaven, says the Lord;
Sacred Heart A	___Take my yoke upon you, ... says the Lord;
Sacred Heart B	(Option A) Take my yoke upon you, ... says the Lord;
	(Option B) God first ... loved_____ us
Sacred Heart C	(Option A) Take my yoke upon you, ... says the Lord;
	(Option B) I am the good shepherd, ... says the Lord;
Christ the King ABC	Blessed is he who comes in the name ... of the Lord!

(F♯m/A)   (Bm)   (Em7)   (A)
 Am/C   Dm   Gm7   C

to God who is, who was, and who is .... to come.
whoever eats this bread will live .... for - ever.
___and learn from me, for I am meek and humble ... of heart.
(Option A) and learn from me, for I am meek and humble ... of heart.
(Option B) and sent his Son as expiation for ... our sins.
(Option A) and learn from me, for I am meek and humble ... of heart.
(Option B) I know my sheep, and mine ... know me.
Blessed is the kingdom of our father David that is ... to come!

Al - le - lu - ia.

A separate assembly response may be found on page 278.

235

ORDINARY TIME A
Sundays 2–7

ACCLAMATION: All (♩ = *ca. 75*)

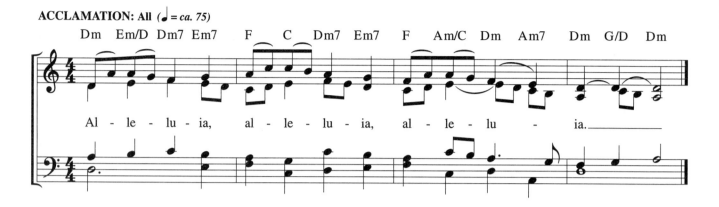

Al - le - lu - ia, al - le - lu - ia, al - le - lu - ia.

VERSE: Cantor or SATB

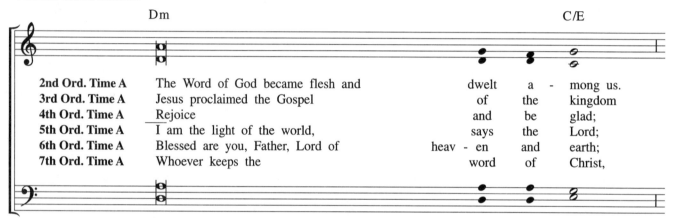

2nd Ord. Time A	The Word of God became flesh and ... dwelt a - mong us.
3rd Ord. Time A	Jesus proclaimed the Gospel ... of the kingdom
4th Ord. Time A	Rejoice ... and be glad;
5th Ord. Time A	I am the light of the world, ... says the Lord;
6th Ord. Time A	Blessed are you, Father, Lord of ... heav - en and earth;
7th Ord. Time A	Whoever keeps the ... word of Christ,

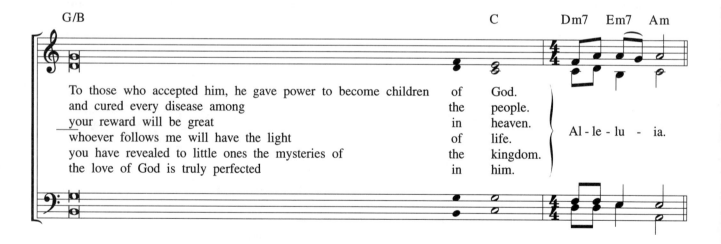

To those who accepted him, he gave power to become children of God.
and cured every disease among the people.
your reward will be great in heaven.
whoever follows me will have the light of life.
you have revealed to little ones the mysteries of the kingdom.
the love of God is truly perfected in him.

Al - le - lu - ia.

A separate assembly response may be found on page 278.

ORDINARY TIME A
Sundays 8–12

ACCLAMATION: All (♩ = ca. 75)

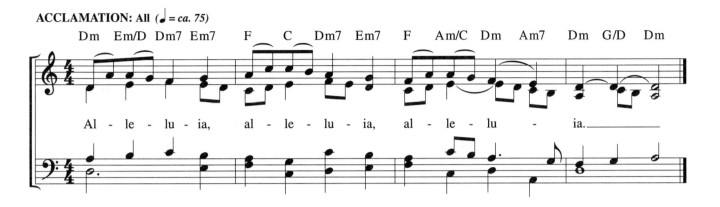

Al - le - lu - ia, al - le - lu - ia, al - le - lu - ia._____

VERSE: Cantor or SATB

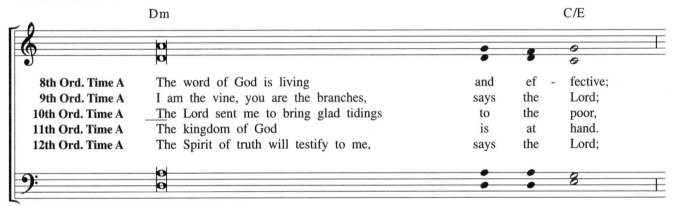

8th Ord. Time A	The word of God is living	and ef - fective;
9th Ord. Time A	I am the vine, you are the branches,	says the Lord;
10th Ord. Time A	The Lord sent me to bring glad tidings	to the poor,
11th Ord. Time A	The kingdom of God	is at hand.
12th Ord. Time A	The Spirit of truth will testify to me,	says the Lord;

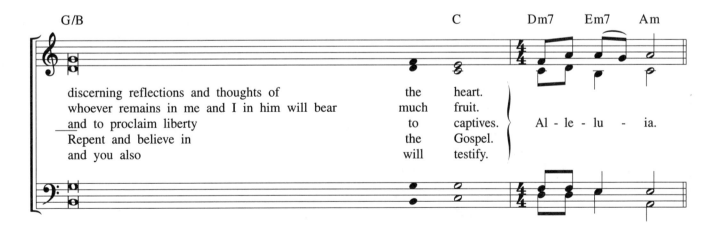

discerning reflections and thoughts of the heart.
whoever remains in me and I in him will bear much fruit.
and to proclaim liberty to captives.
Repent and believe in the Gospel.
and you also will testify.

Al - le - lu - ia.

A separate assembly response may be found on page 278.

ORDINARY TIME A
Sundays 13–17

ACCLAMATION: All (♩ *= ca. 75*)

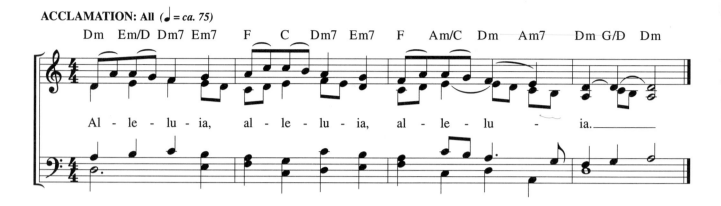

Al - le - lu - ia, al - le - lu - ia, al - le - lu - ia._____

VERSE: Cantor or SATB

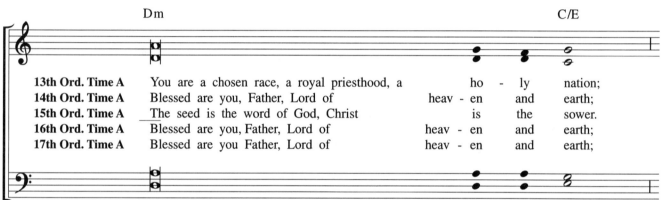

13th Ord. Time A	You are a chosen race, a royal priesthood, a ho - ly nation;
14th Ord. Time A	Blessed are you, Father, Lord of heav - en and earth;
15th Ord. Time A	The seed is the word of God, Christ is the sower.
16th Ord. Time A	Blessed are you, Father, Lord of heav - en and earth;
17th Ord. Time A	Blessed are you Father, Lord of heav - en and earth;

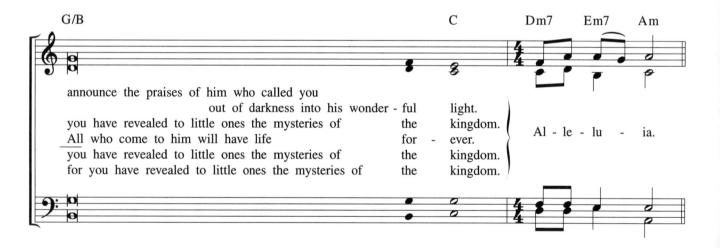

announce the praises of him who called you out of darkness into his wonder - ful light.
you have revealed to little ones the mysteries of the kingdom.
All who come to him will have life for - ever.
you have revealed to little ones the mysteries of the kingdom.
for you have revealed to little ones the mysteries of the kingdom.

Al - le - lu - ia.

A separate assembly response may be found on page 278.

ORDINARY TIME A
Sundays 18–23

ACCLAMATION: All (♩ = *ca. 75*)

Al - le - lu - ia, al - le - lu - ia, al - le - lu - ia.

VERSE: Cantor or SATB

18th Ord. Time A	One does not live on bread a - lone,
19th Ord. Time A	I wait for the Lord;
20th Ord. Time A	Jesus proclaimed the Gospel of the kingdom
21st Ord. Time A	You are Peter and upon this rock I will build my Church
22nd Ord. Time A	May the Father of our Lord Jesus Christ enlighten the eyes of our hearts,
23rd Ord. Time A	God was reconciling the world to himself in Christ

but on every word that comes forth from the mouth of God.
my soul waits for his word.
and cured every disease among the people.
and the gates of the netherworld shall not prevail a - gainst it.
that we may know what is the hope that belongs to our call.
and entrusting to us the message of reconcil - i - ation.

Al - le - lu - ia.

A separate assembly response may be found on page 278.

ORDINARY TIME A
Sundays 24–28

ACCLAMATION: All (♩ = *ca. 75*)

Al - le - lu - ia, al - le - lu - ia, al - le - lu - ia.___

VERSE: Cantor or SATB

24th Ord. Time A	I give you a new commandment, says the ... Lord;
25th Ord. Time A	Open our hearts, O ... Lord,
26th Ord. Time A	My sheep hear my voice, says the ... Lord;
27th Ord. Time A	I have chosen you from the world, says the ... Lord,
28th Ord. Time A	May the Father of Our Lord Jesus Christ enlighten the eyes of our ... hearts,

love one another as I have loved you.
to listen to the words of your Son.
I know them, and they fol - low me.   Al - le - lu - ia.
to go and bear fruit that will re - main.
so that we may know what is the hope that belongs to our call.

A separate assembly response may be found on page 278.

ORDINARY TIME A
Sundays 29–33

ACCLAMATION: All (♩ = *ca. 75*)

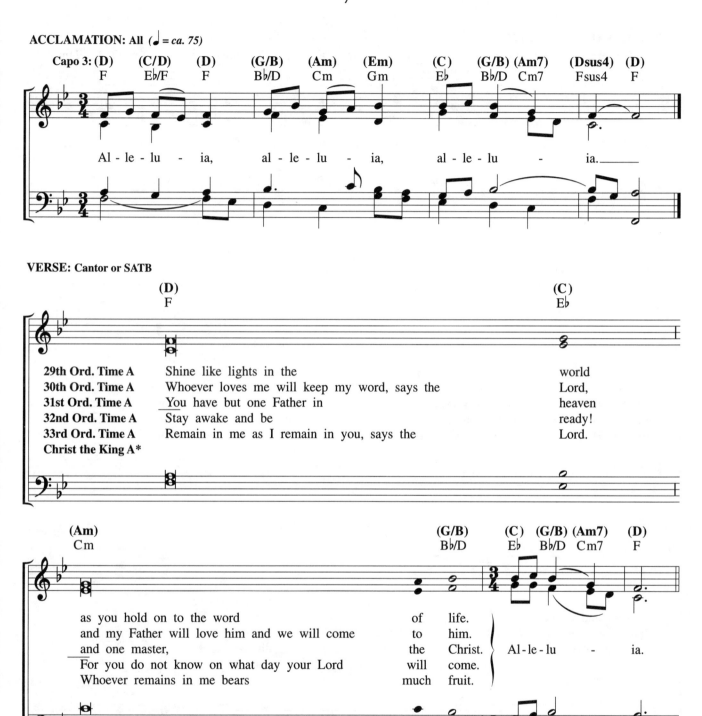

VERSE: Cantor or SATB

29th Ord. Time A	Shine like lights in the world
30th Ord. Time A	Whoever loves me will keep my word, says the Lord,
31st Ord. Time A	You have but one Father in heaven
32nd Ord. Time A	Stay awake and be ready!
33rd Ord. Time A	Remain in me as I remain in you, says the Lord.
Christ the King A*	

as you hold on to the word of life.
and my Father will love him and we will come to him.
and one master, the Christ.
For you do not know on what day your Lord will come.
Whoever remains in me bears much fruit.

Al-le-lu - ia.

*May be found on page 235.
A separate assembly response may be found on page 278.

ORDINARY TIME B
Sundays 2–7

ACCLAMATION: All (♩ *= ca. 75*)

Al - le - lu - ia, al - le - lu - ia, al - le - lu - ia. ____

VERSE: Cantor or SATB

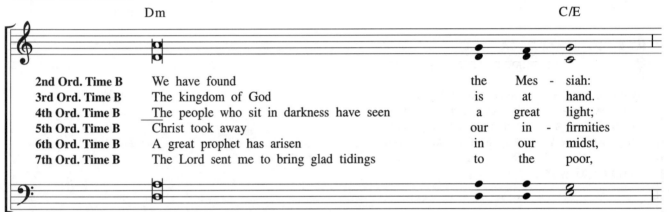

2nd Ord. Time B	We have found the Mes - siah:
3rd Ord. Time B	The kingdom of God is at hand.
4th Ord. Time B	The people who sit in darkness have seen a great light;
5th Ord. Time B	Christ took away our in - firmities
6th Ord. Time B	A great prophet has arisen in our midst,
7th Ord. Time B	The Lord sent me to bring glad tidings to the poor,

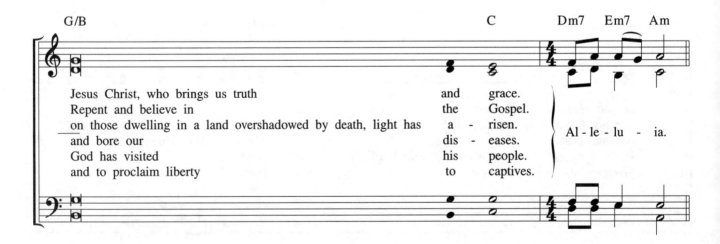

Jesus Christ, who brings us truth and grace.
Repent and believe in the Gospel.
on those dwelling in a land overshadowed by death, light has a - risen.
and bore our dis - eases.
God has visited his people.
and to proclaim liberty to captives.

Al - le - lu - ia.

A separate assembly response may be found on page 278.

ORDINARY TIME B
Sundays 8–12

ACCLAMATION: All (♩ *= ca. 75*)

Al - le - lu - ia, al - le - lu - ia, al - le - lu - ia._____

VERSE: Cantor or SATB

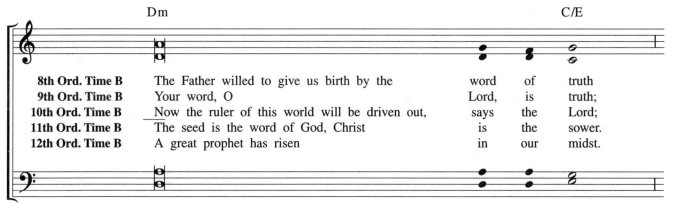

8th Ord. Time B	The Father willed to give us birth by the word of truth
9th Ord. Time B	Your word, O Lord, is truth;
10th Ord. Time B	Now the ruler of this world will be driven out, says the Lord;
11th Ord. Time B	The seed is the word of God, Christ is the sower.
12th Ord. Time B	A great prophet has risen in our midst.

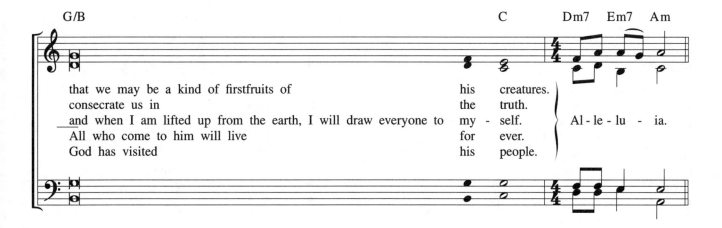

that we may be a kind of firstfruits of his creatures.
consecrate us in the truth.
and when I am lifted up from the earth, I will draw everyone to my - self. Al - le - lu - ia.
All who come to him will live for ever.
God has visited his people.

A separate assembly response may be found on page 278.

ORDINARY TIME B
Sundays 13–17

ACCLAMATION: All (♩ = *ca. 75*)

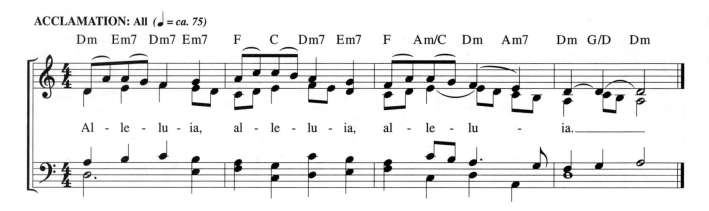

Al - le - lu - ia, al - le - lu - ia, al - le - lu - ia._____

VERSE: Cantor or SATB

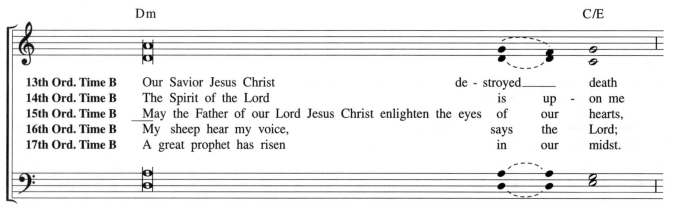

13th Ord. Time B	Our Savior Jesus Christ	de - stroyed_____ death
14th Ord. Time B	The Spirit of the Lord	is up - on me
15th Ord. Time B	May the Father of our Lord Jesus Christ enlighten the eyes	of our hearts,
16th Ord. Time B	My sheep hear my voice,	says the Lord;
17th Ord. Time B	A great prophet has risen	in our midst.

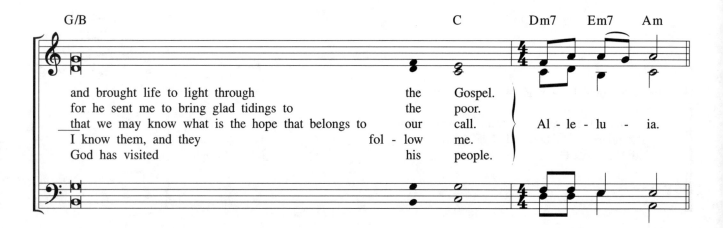

and brought life to light through the Gospel.
for he sent me to bring glad tidings to the poor.
that we may know what is the hope that belongs to our call. Al - le - lu - ia.
I know them, and they fol - low me.
God has visited his people.

A separate assembly response may be found on page 278.

ORDINARY TIME B
Sundays 18–23

ACCLAMATION: All (♩ = *ca.* 75)

VERSE: Cantor or SATB

18th Ord. Time B	One does not live on bread a - lone,
19th Ord. Time B	I am the living bread that came down from heaven, says the Lord;
20th Ord. Time B	Whoever eats my flesh and drinks my blood
21st Ord. Time B	Your words, Lord, are Spirit and life;
22nd Ord. Time B	The Father willed to give us birth by the word of truth
23rd Ord. Time B	Jesus proclaimed the Gospel of the kingdom

but on every word that comes forth from the mouth of God.
whoever eats this bread will live for - ever.
remains in me and I in him, says the Lord.
you have the words of everlast - ing life.
that we may be a kind of firstfruits of his creatures.
and cured every disease among the people.

Al - le - lu - ia.

A separate assembly response may be found on page 278.

ORDINARY TIME B
Sundays 24–28

ACCLAMATION: All (♩ = ca. 75)

Al - le - lu - ia, al - le - lu - ia, al - le - lu - ia.___

VERSE: Cantor or SATB

24th Ord. Time B	May I never boast except in the cross of our — Lord
25th Ord. Time B	God has called us through the — Gospel
26th Ord. Time B	Your word, O Lord, is — truth;
27th Ord. Time B	If we love one another, God remains in — us
28th Ord. Time B	Blessed are the poor in — spirit,

through which the world has been crucified to me and I to the world.
to possess the glory of our Lord Je - sus Christ.
consecrate us in the truth.   Al - le - lu - ia.
and his love is brought to perfection in us.
for theirs is the kingdom of heaven.

A separate assembly response may be found on page 278.

ACCLAMATION: All (♩= *ca. 75*)

VERSE: Cantor or SATB

29th Ord. Time B	The Son of Man came to ... serve
30th Ord. Time B	Our Savior Jesus Christ destroyed ... death
31st Ord. Time B	Whoever loves me will keep my word, says the ... Lord;
32nd Ord. Time B	Blessed are the poor in ... spirit,
33rd Ord. Time B	Be vigilant at all ... times
Christ the King B*	

and to give his life as a ransom ... for many.
and brought life to light through ... the Gospel.
and my Father will love him and we will come ... to him. } Al-le-lu - ia.
for theirs is the kingdom ... of heaven.
and pray that you have the strength to stand before the Son of Man.

*May be found on page 235.
 A separate assembly response may be found on page 278.

ORDINARY TIME C
Sundays 2–7

ACCLAMATION: All (♩ = *ca. 75*)

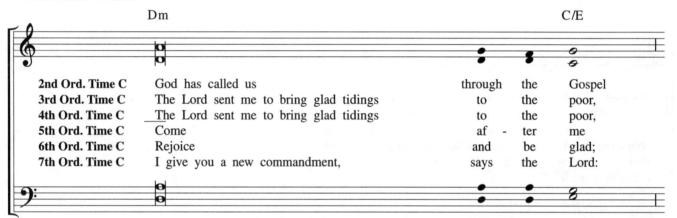

Al - le - lu - ia, al - le - lu - ia, al - le - lu - ia.___

VERSE: Cantor or SATB

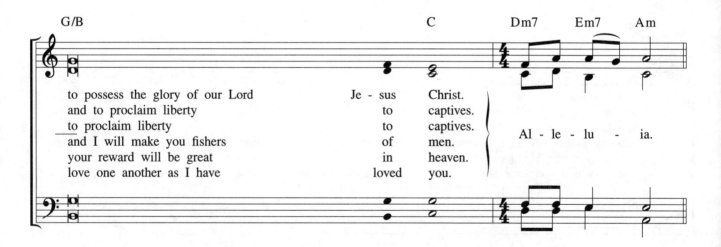

2nd Ord. Time C	God has called us	through the	Gospel
3rd Ord. Time C	The Lord sent me to bring glad tidings	to the	poor,
4th Ord. Time C	The Lord sent me to bring glad tidings	to the	poor,
5th Ord. Time C	Come	af - ter	me
6th Ord. Time C	Rejoice	and be	glad;
7th Ord. Time C	I give you a new commandment,	says the	Lord:

to possess the glory of our Lord Je - sus Christ.
and to proclaim liberty to captives.
to proclaim liberty to captives.
and I will make you fishers of men.
your reward will be great in heaven.
love one another as I have loved you.

Al - le - lu - ia.

A separate assembly response may be found on page 278.

ORDINARY TIME C
Sundays 8–12

ACCLAMATION: All (♩ = *ca. 75*)

Al - le - lu - ia, al - le - lu - ia, al - le - lu - ia.___

VERSE: Cantor or SATB

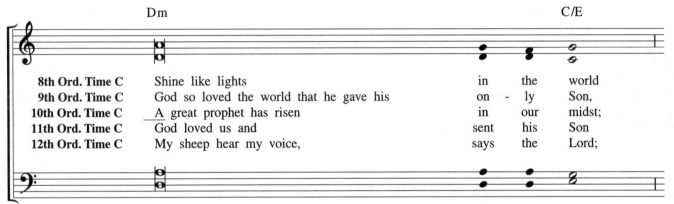

8th Ord. Time C	Shine like lights	in the world
9th Ord. Time C	God so loved the world that he gave his	on - ly Son,
10th Ord. Time C	A great prophet has risen	in our midst;
11th Ord. Time C	God loved us and	sent his Son
12th Ord. Time C	My sheep hear my voice,	says the Lord;

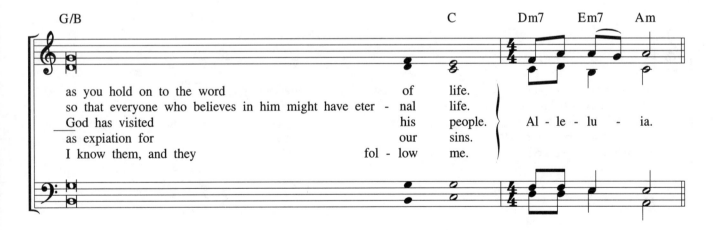

as you hold on to the word of life.
so that everyone who believes in him might have eter - nal life.
God has visited his people. } Al - le - lu - ia.
as expiation for our sins.
I know them, and they fol - low me.

A separate assembly response may be found on page 278.

ORDINARY TIME C
Sundays 13–17

ACCLAMATION: All (♩ = *ca. 75*)

Al - le - lu - ia, al - le - lu - ia, al - le - lu - ia.____

VERSE: Cantor or SATB

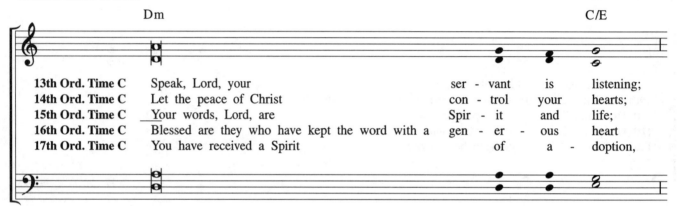

13th Ord. Time C	Speak, Lord, your ... ser - vant is listening;
14th Ord. Time C	Let the peace of Christ ... con - trol your hearts;
15th Ord. Time C	Your words, Lord, are ... Spir - it and life;
16th Ord. Time C	Blessed are they who have kept the word with a gen - er - ous heart
17th Ord. Time C	You have received a Spirit ... of a - doption,

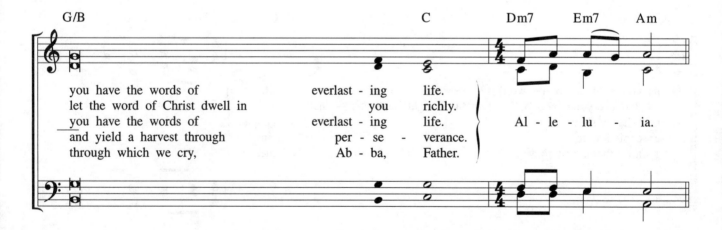

you have the words of everlast - ing life.
let the word of Christ dwell in you richly.
you have the words of everlast - ing life.
and yield a harvest through per - se - verance.
through which we cry, Ab - ba, Father.

Al - le - lu - ia.

A separate assembly response may be found on page 278.

ORDINARY TIME C
Sundays 18–23

ACCLAMATION: All (♩ = *ca. 75*)

VERSE: Cantor or SATB

18th Ord. Time C	Blessed are the poor in spirit,
19th Ord. Time C	Stay awake and be ready!
20th Ord. Time C	My sheep hear my voice, says the Lord;
21st Ord. Time C	I am the way, the truth and the life, says the Lord;
22nd Ord. Time C	Take my yoke upon you, says the Lord,
23rd Ord. Time C	Let your face shine upon your servant;

for theirs is the kingdom of heaven.
For you do not know on what day the Son of Man will come.
I know them, and they fol - low me.
no one comes to the Father, except through me.
and learn from me, for I am meek and humble of heart.
and teach me your laws.

Al - le - lu - ia.

A separate assembly response may be found on page 278.

ORDINARY TIME C
Sundays 24–28

ACCLAMATION: All (♩ = *ca. 75*)

VERSE: Cantor or SATB

24th Ord. Time C	God was reconciling the world to himself in ... Christ
25th Ord. Time C	Though our Lord Jesus Christ was rich, he became ... poor,
26th Ord. Time C	Though our Lord Jesus Christ was rich, he became ... poor,
27th Ord. Time C	The word of the Lord remains for ... ever.
28th Ord. Time C	In all circumstances, give ... thanks,

and entrusting to us the message of reconcil - i - ation.
so that by his poverty you might be - come rich.
so that by his poverty you might be - come rich. Al - le - lu - ia.
This is the word that has been proclaimed to you.
for this is the will of God for you in Christ Jesus.

A separate assembly response may be found on page 278.

ORDINARY TIME C
Sundays 29–33

ACCLAMATION: All (♩ = ca. 75)

Al - le - lu - ia, al - le - lu - ia, al - le - lu - ia.___

VERSE: Cantor or SATB

29th Ord. Time C	The word of God is living and ... ef - fective,
30th Ord. Time C	God was reconciling the world to himself in ... Christ,
31st Ord. Time C	God so loved the world that he gave his only ... Son,
32nd Ord. Time C	Jesus Christ is the firstborn of the ... dead;
33rd Ord. Time C	Stand erect and raise your ... heads
Christ the King C*	

discerning reflections and thoughts of ... the heart.
and entrusting to us the message of ... sal - vation.
so that everyone who believes in him might have eter - nal life.   Al - le - lu - ia.
to him be glory and power, forever ... and ever.
because your redemption is ... at hand.

*May be found on page 235.
A separate assembly response may be found on page 278.

SOLEMNITIES AND FEASTS OF THE LORD AND THE SAINTS
Presentation, St. Joseph, Annunciation and St. John the Baptist

ACCLAMATION (♩ = ca. 95)

Descant: Al - le - lu - ia,___ al - le - lu - ia, al - le - lu - ia.___

All: Al - le - lu - ia, al - le - lu - ia, al - le - lu - ia.

VERSE: Cantor or SATB

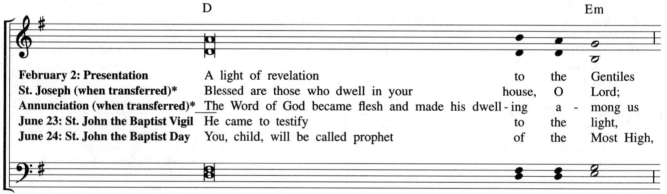

February 2: Presentation	A light of revelation to the Gentiles
St. Joseph (when transferred)*	Blessed are those who dwell in your house, O Lord;
Annunciation (when transferred)*	The Word of God became flesh and made his dwell-ing a - mong us
June 23: St. John the Baptist Vigil	He came to testify to the light,
June 24: St. John the Baptist Day	You, child, will be called prophet of the Most High,

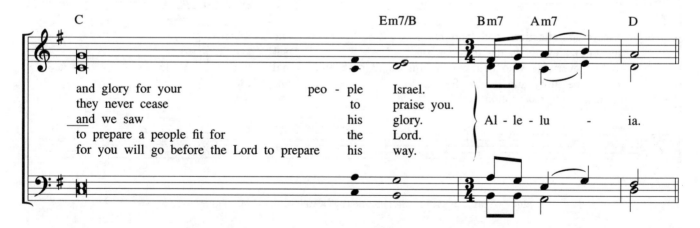

and glory for your peo - ple Israel.
they never cease to praise you.
and we saw his glory. Al - le - lu - ia.
to prepare a people fit for the Lord.
for you will go before the Lord to prepare his way.

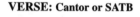

*When the Solemnity of St. Joseph, Husband of the Blessed Virgin Mary or the Solemnity of the Annunciation of the Lord falls within Holy Week or Easter Week, its office is transferred to the Monday after the octave of Easter.

A separate assembly response may be found on page 278.

SOLEMNITIES AND FEASTS OF THE LORD AND THE SAINTS
St. Joseph and Annunciation

ACCLAMATION: All (♩ = ca. 60)

Praise to you, Lord Jesus Christ, King of end-less glo-ry!

OR

ACCLAMATION: All (♩ = ca. 85)

Glo-ry to you, Word of God, Lord Je-sus Christ!

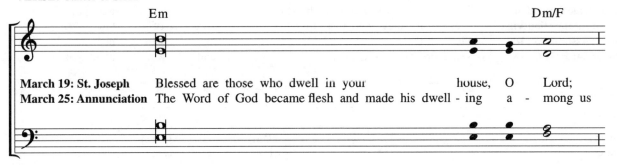

VERSE: Cantor or SATB

March 19: St. Joseph Blessed are those who dwell in your house, O Lord;

March 25: Annunciation The Word of God became flesh and made his dwell-ing a - mong us

they never cease to praise you.

and we saw his glory.

A separate assembly response may be found on page 278.

SOLEMNITIES AND FEASTS OF THE LORD AND THE SAINTS
Ss. Peter and Paul, Transfiguration, Assumption and Holy Cross

A separate assembly response may be found on page 278.

SOLEMNITIES AND FEASTS OF THE LORD AND THE SAINTS
All Saints and All Souls

ACCLAMATION (♩. = *ca. 40*)

Descant: Al - le - lu - ia, al - le - lu - ia, al - le - lu - ia.

Capo 3: (D) (A) (Em) (Bm) (F♯m) (F♯m/A) (Em7/G) (D)
F C Gm Dm Am Am/C Gm7/B♭ F

All: Al - le - lu - ia, al - le - lu - ia, al - le - lu - ia.

VERSE: Cantor or SATB

(D) (A)
F C

November 1: All Saints	Come to me, all you who labor and are burdened,
November 2: All Souls (Option 1)	Come, you who are blessed by my Father;
(Option 2)	God so loved the world that he gave us his on - ly Son
(Option 3)	This is the will of my Father, says the Lord,
(Option 4)	I am the living bread that came down from heaven, says the Lord;
(Option 5)	I am the resurrection and the life, says the Lord;

(F♯m/A) (Bm) (Em7) (A)
Am/C Dm Gm7 C

and I will give you rest, says the Lord.
inherit the kingdom prepared for you from the foundation of the world.
so that everyone who sees the Son and believes in him may have eter-nal life.
that everyone who sees the Son and believes in him may have eter-nal life.
whoever eats this bread will live for - ever.
whoever believes in me will nev-er die.

Al - le - lu - ia.

A separate assembly response may be found on page 278.

SOLEMNITIES AND FEASTS OF THE LORD AND THE SAINTS

St. Martin de Porres, Dedication of the Lateran Basilica,
Immaculate Conception and Our Lady of Guadalupe

A separate assembly response may be found on page 278.

Rite of Entrance into the Order of Catechumens and Thanksgiving Day

ACCLAMATION: All (♩ = ca. 75)

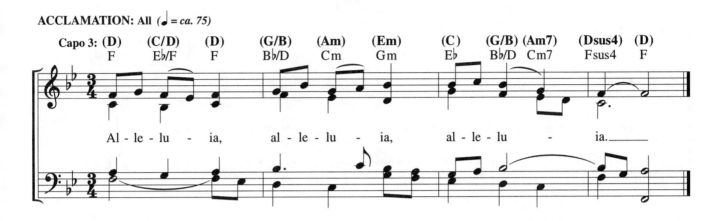

Al - le - lu - ia, al - le - lu - ia, al - le - lu - ia.

VERSE: Cantor or SATB

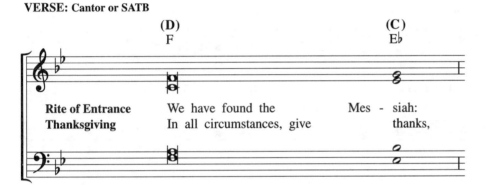

Rite of Entrance   We have found the   Mes - siah:
Thanksgiving   In all circumstances, give   thanks,

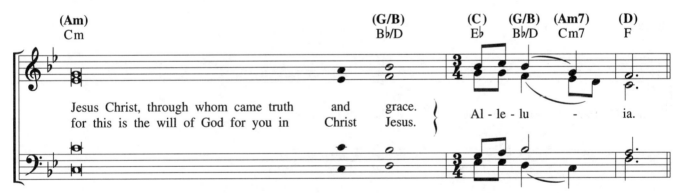

Jesus Christ, through whom came truth   and   grace.   Al - le - lu - ia.
for this is the will of God for you in   Christ   Jesus.

A separate assembly response may be found on page 278.

RITE OF ENTRANCE INTO
THE ORDER OF CATECHUMENS
(Lent)

ACCLAMATION: All (𝅗𝅥 = *ca. 60*)

Praise to you, Lord Je - sus Christ, King of end - less glo - ry!

OR

ACCLAMATION: All (♩ = *ca. 85*)

Glo - ry to you, Word of God, Lord Je - sus Christ!

VERSE: Cantor or SATB

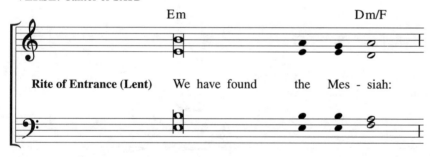

Rite of Entrance (Lent) We have found the Mes - siah:

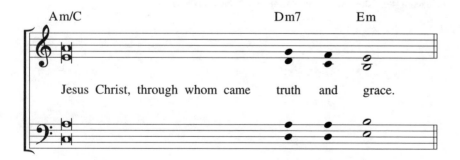

Jesus Christ, through whom came truth and grace.

A separate assembly response may be found on page 278.

ASSEMBLY RESPONSES

RESPONSORIAL PSALMS, A–Bl

Psalm 97

℟. A light will shine on us this day: the Lord is born for us.

Psalm 146

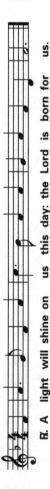

℟. Bless'd are the poor in spir-it; the king-dom of heav'n is theirs!

Psalm 98

℟. All the ends of the earth have seen the sav - ing pow-er of God.

Psalm 84

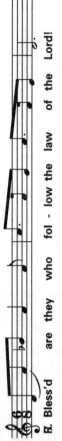

℟. Bless - ed are they who dwell in your house, O Lord.

Psalm 118 -

℟. Al - le - lu - ia, al - le - lu - ia, al - le - lu - ia.

Psalm 119

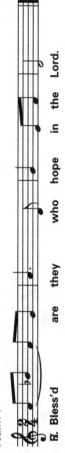

℟. Bless'd are they who fol - low the law of the Lord!

Psalm 51

℟. Be mer - ci - ful, O Lord, for we have sinned.

Psalm 1

℟. Bless'd are they who hope in the Lord.

Psalm 91

℟. Be with me, Lord, when I am in trou - ble.

Psalm 128

℟. Bless'd are those who fear the Lord.

RESPONSORIAL PSALMS, BL–FI

Psalm 128

℟. Bless - ed are those who fear the Lord and walk in his ways.

Psalm 113

℟. Bless'd be the name of the Lord for ev - er.

Psalm 33

℟. Bless'd the peo - ple the Lord has cho - sen to be his own.

Psalm 51

℟. Cre - ate a clean heart in me, O God.

Isaiah 12

℟. Cry out with joy and glad - ness: for a - mong you is the great and Ho - ly One of Is - ra - el.

Psalm 78

℟. Do not for - get the works of the Lord!

Psalm 31

℟. [Fa - ther,] Fa - ther, [in - to your hands.] in - to your hands I com - mend my spir - it.

Psalm 90

℟. Fill us with your love, O Lord, and we will sing for joy!

RESPONSORIAL PSALMS, FO–GO

Psalm 117

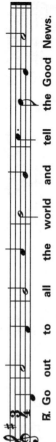

℟. Go out to all the world and tell the Good News.

Psalm 68

℟. God, in your good - ness, you have made a home for the poor.

Psalm 47

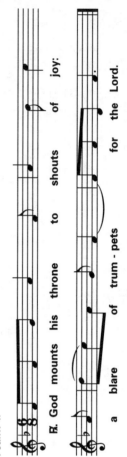

℟. God mounts his throne to shouts of joy. [to shouts of joy.]

Psalm 47

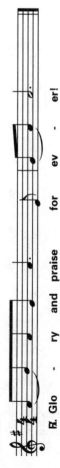

a blare of trum - pets for the Lord.

℟. God mounts his throne to shouts of joy:

Psalm 89

℟. For ev - er I will sing the good - ness of the Lord.

Psalm 118

℟. Give thanks to the Lord for he is good, his love is ev - er - last - ing.

Psalm 107

℟. Give thanks to the Lord, his love is ev - er - last - ing, [ev - er - last - ing.]

Psalm 96

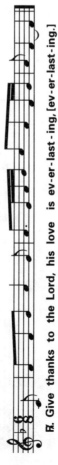

℟. Give the Lord glo - ry and hon - or.

Daniel 3

℟. Glo - ry and praise for ev - er!

RESPONSORIAL PSALMS, GO–I

Psalm 136

℟. God's love is ev - er - last - ing.

Psalm 18

℟. [I love you,] I love you, Lord, my strength.

Psalm 15

℟. He who does jus - tice will live in the pres - ence of the Lord.

Psalm 139

I praise you for I am won - der - ful - ly made.

Psalm 40

℟. Here am I, Lord; I come to do your will.

Psalm 23

℟. I shall live in the house of the Lord all the days of my life.

Psalm 27

℟. I be - lieve that I shall see the good things of the Lord in the land of the liv - ing.

Psalm 32

℟. I turn to you, Lord, in time of trou - ble, and you fill me with the joy of sal - va - tion.

Responsorial Psalms, I–If

Psalm 34

℟. [I will bless the Lord,] I will bless the Lord at all times.

Psalm 30

℟. I will praise you, Lord, for you have res - cued me.

Psalm 22
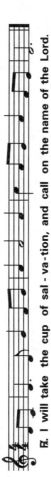
℟. I will praise you, Lord, in the as - sem - bly of your peo - ple.

Psalm 71

℟. I will sing of your sal - va - tion, [sing of your sal - va - tion.]

Psalm 116

℟. I will take the cup of sal - va - tion, and call on the name of the Lord.

Psalm 116

℟. I will walk be - fore the Lord, in the land of the liv - ing.

Psalm 145
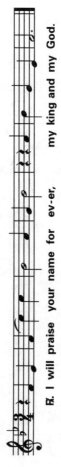
℟. I will praise your name for ev - er, my king and my God.

Psalm 95

℟. If to - day you hear his voice, hard - en not your hearts.

Psalm 51

℟. I will rise and go to my fa - ther.

RESPONSORIAL PSALMS, IN–LE

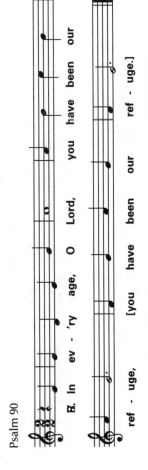

Psalm 90

℟. In ev - 'ry age, O Lord, you have been our ref - uge, [you have been our ref - uge.]

Psalm 66

℟. Let all the earth cry out to God with joy.

Psalm 66

℟. Let all the earth cry out to God with joy, al - le - lu - ia.

Psalm 138

℟. In the sight of the an - gels I will sing your prais - es, Lord.

Psalm 137

℟. Let my tongue be si - lenced, if I ev - er for - get you!

Psalm 131

℟. In you, Lord, I have found my peace, [I have found my peace.]

Psalm 24

℟. Let the Lord en - ter; he is king of glo - ry.

Psalm 72

℟. Jus - tice shall flour - ish in his time, and full - ness of peace for ev - er.

Psalm 122

℟. Let us go re - joic - ing to the house of the Lord.

RESPONSORIAL PSALMS, LE–LO

Exodus 15

℟. Let us sing to the Lord; he has cov - ered him - self in glo - ry, [in glo - ry.]

Psalm 40

℟.[Lord,] Lord, come to my aid! [Come to my aid!]

Psalm 42/43

℟. Like a deer that longs for run - ning streams, my soul longs for you, my God.

Psalm 72

℟. Lord, ev-'ry na-tion on earth will a - dore you, [will a - dore you.]

Psalm 32

℟. for - give the wrong I have done.

Psalm 31

℟. Lord, be my rock of safe - ty.

Psalm 132

℟. Lord, go up to the place of your rest, you and the ark of your ho - li - ness.

Psalm 146

℟. [Lord,] Lord, come and save us, [come and save us.]

Psalm 41

℟. Lord, heal my soul, for I have sinned a - gainst you.

RESPONSORIAL PSALMS, LO

Psalm 33

R. Lord, let your mer-cy be on us, as we place our trust in you.

Psalm 80

R. Lord, make us turn to you; let us see your face and we shall be saved.

Psalm 138

R. Lord, on the day I called for help, you an-swered me.

Psalm 104

R. Lord, send out your Spir-it, and re-new the face of the earth.

Psalm 85

R. [Lord,] Lord, show us your mer-cy and love, [your mer-cy and love.]

Psalm 119

R. Lord, I love your com-mands, [I love your com-mands.]

Psalm 69

R. Lord, in your great love, an-swer me, [an-swer me.]

Psalm 92

R. Lord, it is good to give thanks to you.

Psalm 85

R. Lord, let us see your kind-ness, and grant us your sal - va - tion.

Psalm 4

R. Lord, let your face shine on us.

Responsorial Psalms, Lo–My

Psalm 24

℟. Lord, this is the peo-ple that longs to see your face.

Psalm 138

℟. Lord, your love is e-ter-nal; do not for-sake the work of your hands.

Psalm 17

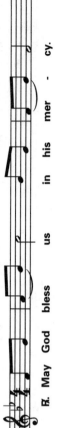

℟. Lord, when your glo-ry ap-pears, my joy will be full.

Psalm 67

℟. May God bless us in his mer-cy.

Psalm 86

℟. Lord, you are good and for-giv-ing. [good and for-giv-ing.]

Psalm 128

℟. May the Lord bless us all the days of our lives.

Psalm 19

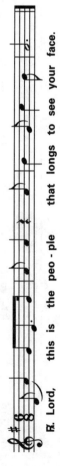

℟. Lord, you have the words of ev-er-last-ing life.

Psalm 22

℟. My God, my God, why have you a-ban-doned me?

Psalm 16

℟. Lord, you will show us the path of life.

Psalm 63

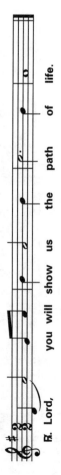

℟. My soul is thirst-ing for you, O Lord my God.

RESPONSORIAL PSALMS, MY–PR

Luke 1

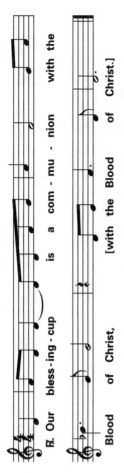

℟. My soul re - joic - es in my God.

Psalm 25

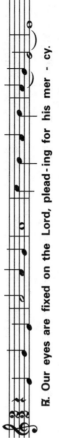

℟. No one who waits for you, O Lord, will ev - er be put to shame.

Psalm 104

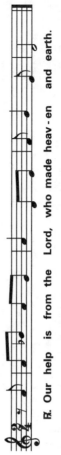

℟. [O bless the Lord, O bless the Lord,] O bless the Lord, my soul.

Psalm 67

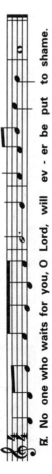

℟. O God, let all the na - tions praise you!

Psalm 8

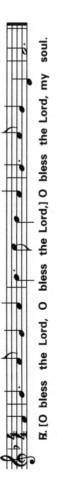

℟. O Lord, our God, how won-der-ful your name in all the earth!

Psalm 116

℟. Our bless-ing-cup is a com-mu-nion with the Blood of Christ, [with the Blood of Christ.]

Psalm 123

℟. Our eyes are fixed on the Lord, plead-ing for his mer - cy.

Psalm 121

℟. Our help is from the Lord, who made heav - en and earth.

Psalm 147

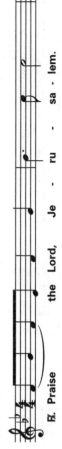

℟. Praise the Lord, Je - ru - sa - lem.

RESPONSORIAL PSALMS, PR–TA

Psalm 146

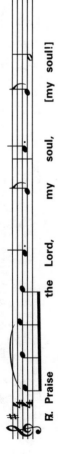

℟. Praise the Lord, my soul, [my soul!]

Psalm 62

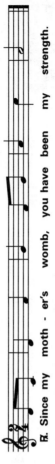

℟. Rest in God a - lone, my soul.

Psalm 147

℟. Praise the Lord, who heals the bro - ken - heart - ed.

Psalm 71

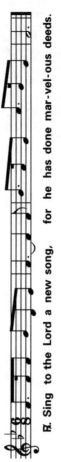

℟. Since my moth - er's womb, you have been my strength.

Psalm 113

℟. Praise the Lord who lifts up the poor.

Psalm 98

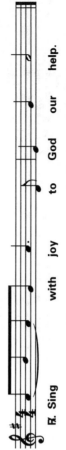

℟. Sing to the Lord a new song, for he has done mar-vel-ous deeds.

Psalm 96

℟. Pro-claim his mar - vel-ous deeds to all the na - tions.

Psalm 81

℟. Sing with joy to God our help.

Psalm 25

℟. [Re-mem - ber,] re-mem - ber your mer - cies, O Lord.

Psalm 34

℟. [Taste and see,] taste and see the good-ness of the Lord.

Responsorial Psalms, Te–Th

Psalm 25

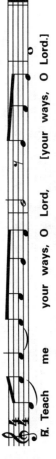

℟. Teach me your ways, O Lord, [your ways, O Lord.]

Psalm 34

℟. The an-gel of the Lord will res-cue those who fear him.

Psalm 33

℟. The earth is full of [the good-ness,] the good-ness of the Lord.

Psalm 145

℟. The hand of the Lord feeds us; he an-swers all our needs.

Psalm 112

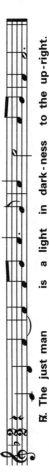

℟. The just man is a light in dark-ness to the up-right.

Psalm 98

℟. The Lord comes to rule the earth with jus-tice.

Psalm 78

℟. The Lord gave them bread from heav-en.

Psalm 126

℟. The Lord has done great things for us; we are filled with joy.

Psalm 98

℟. The Lord has re-vealed to the na-tions his sav-ing pow-er.

Psalm 103

℟. The Lord has set his throne in heav-en.

RESPONSORIAL PSALMS, TH

Psalm 34

℟. The Lord hears the cry of the poor, [the cry of the poor.]

The English translation of the psalm response from the *Lectionary for Mass*, © 1969, 1981, 1997, International Committee on English in the Liturgy, Inc. All rights reserved. Used with permission. Music © 2001, John Schiavone. Published by OCP Publications, 5536 NE Hassalo, Portland, OR 97213. All rights reserved.

Psalm 97

℟. The Lord is king, the Most High o - ver all the earth.

The English translation of the psalm response from the *Lectionary for Mass*, © 1969, 1981, 1997, International Committee on English in the Liturgy, Inc. All rights reserved. Used with permission. Music © 2001, John Schiavone. Published by OCP Publications, 5536 NE Hassalo, Portland, OR 97213. All rights reserved.

Psalm 103

℟. The Lord is kind and mer - ci - ful, [kind and mer - ci - ful.]

The English translation of the psalm response from the *Lectionary for Mass*, © 1969, 1981, 1997, International Committee on English in the Liturgy, Inc. All rights reserved. Used with permission. Music © 2001, John Schiavone. Published by OCP Publications, 5536 NE Hassalo, Portland, OR 97213. All rights reserved.

Psalm 27

℟. The Lord is my light and my sal - va - tion.

The English translation of the psalm response from the *Lectionary for Mass*, © 1969, 1981, 1997, International Committee on English in the Liturgy, Inc. All rights reserved. Used with permission. Music © 2001, John Schiavone. Published by OCP Publications, 5536 NE Hassalo, Portland, OR 97213. All rights reserved.

Psalm 103

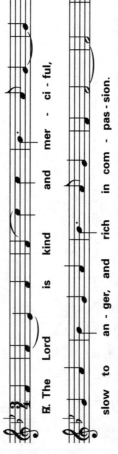

℟. The Lord is kind and mer - ci - ful, slow to an - ger, and rich in com - pas - sion.

The English translation of the psalm response from the *Lectionary for Mass*, © 1969, 1981, 1997, International Committee on English in the Liturgy, Inc. All rights reserved. Used with permission. Music © 2001, John Schiavone. Published by OCP Publications, 5536 NE Hassalo, Portland, OR 97213. All rights reserved.

Psalm 23

℟. The Lord is my shep - herd; there is noth - ing I shall want.

The English translation of the psalm response from the *Lectionary for Mass*, © 1969, 1981, 1997, International Committee on English in the Liturgy, Inc. All rights reserved. Used with permission. Music © 2001, John Schiavone. Published by OCP Publications, 5536 NE Hassalo, Portland, OR 97213. All rights reserved.

Psalm 145

℟. The Lord is near to all who call up - on him.

The English translation of the psalm response from the *Lectionary for Mass*, © 1969, 1981, 1997, International Committee on English in the Liturgy, Inc. All rights reserved. Used with permission. Music © 2001, John Schiavone. Published by OCP Publications, 5536 NE Hassalo, Portland, OR 97213. All rights reserved.

Psalm 93

℟. The Lord is king; he is robed in maj - es - ty.

The English translation of the psalm response from the *Lectionary for Mass*, © 1969, 1981, 1997, International Committee on English in the Liturgy, Inc. All rights reserved. Used with permission. Music © 2001, John Schiavone. Published by OCP Publications, 5536 NE Hassalo, Portland, OR 97213. All rights reserved.

Psalm 105

℟. The Lord re - mem - bers his cov - e - nant for ev - er.

The English translation of the psalm response from the *Lectionary for Mass*, © 1969, 1981, 1997, International Committee on English in the Liturgy, Inc. All rights reserved. Used with permission. Music © 2001, John Schiavone. Published by OCP Publications, 5536 NE Hassalo, Portland, OR 97213. All rights reserved.

Psalm 54

℟. The Lord up - holds my life.

Psalm 29

℟. The Lord will bless his peo - ple with peace.

Psalm 103

℟. The Lord's kind - ness is ev - er - last - ing to those who fear him.

Psalm 15

℟. The one who does jus - tice will live in the pres - ence of the Lord.

Psalm 19

℟. The pre - cepts of the Lord give joy to the heart.

Psalm 45

℟. The queen stands at your right hand, ar - rayed in gold.

Psalm 65

℟. The seed that falls on good ground will yield a fruit - ful har - vest.

Psalm 89

℟. The son of Da - vid will live for ev - er.

Psalm 118

℟. The stone re - ject - ed by the build - ers has be - come the cor - ner - stone.

Psalm 80

℟. The vine - yard of the Lord is the house of Is - ra - el.

Responsorial Psalms, Th–To

Psalm 46

℟. The wa - ters of the riv - er glad - den the cit - y of God,

the ho - ly dwell - ing of the Most High.

Psalm 23

℟. Though I walk in the val - ley of dark - ness,

I fear no e - vil, for you are with me.

Psalm 147

℟. The word of God be - came man and lived a - mong us.

Psalm 50

℟. To the up - right I will show the sav - ing pow'r of God.

Psalm 19

℟. Their mes - sage goes out through all the earth.

Psalm 25

℟. To you, O Lord, I lift my soul, [I lift my soul.]

Psalm 118

℟. This is the day the Lord has made; let us re - joice and be glad.

Psalm 96

℟. [To - day,] to - day is born our Sav - ior, Christ the Lord.

RESPONSORIAL PSALMS, TU–YO

Psalm 69

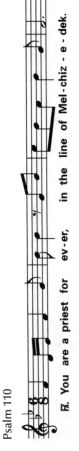

℟. Turn to the Lord in your need, and you will live.

Psalm 110

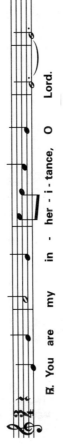

℟. You are a priest for ev-er, in the line of Mel-chiz - e - dek.

Psalm 100

℟. We are his peo-ple: [the sheep of his flock.]

Psalm 16

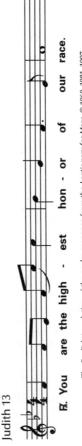

℟. You are my in - her - i - tance, O Lord.

Psalm 24

℟. Who is this king of glo - ry? It is the Lord!

Judith 13

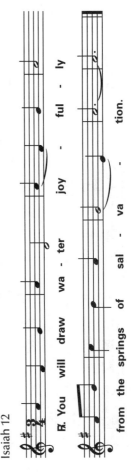

℟. You are the high - est hon - or of our race.

Psalm 130

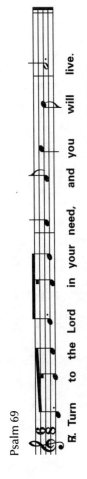

℟. With the Lord there is mer - cy, and full - ness of re - demp - tion, [full - ness of re - demp - tion.]

Isaiah 12

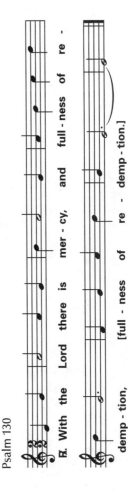

℟. You will draw wa - ter joy - ful - ly from the springs of sal - va - tion.

RESPONSORIAL PSALMS, YO

GOSPEL ACCLAMATIONS (Continued)

Psalm 25

R. Your ways, O Lord, are love and truth to those who keep your cov - e - nant.

R. Al - le - lu - ia, al - le - lu - ia, al - le - lu - ia.

Psalm 19

R. Your words, Lord, are Spir - it and life.

R. Al - le - lu - ia, al - le - lu - ia, al - le - lu - ia.

GOSPEL ACCLAMATIONS

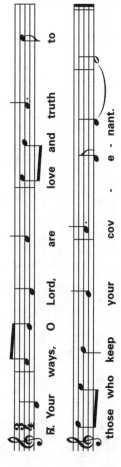

R. Al - le - lu - ia, al - le - lu - ia, al - le - lu - ia.

R. Praise to you, Lord Je - sus Christ, King of end - less glo - ry!

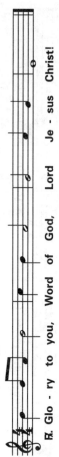

R. Al - le - lu - ia, al - le - lu - ia, al - le - lu - ia.

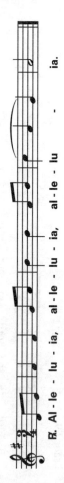

R. Glo - ry to you, Word of God, Lord Je - sus Christ!

INDICES

SCRIPTURAL INDEX

Responsorial Psalms

COMMON (SEASONAL) PSALM INDEX

RITUAL/TOPICAL INDEX

This **Ritual/Topical Index** will assist in locating psalms and gospel acclamations recommended by the Church for occasions other than Sundays, Feast Days and Solemnities. In some instances, while the response is identical, the verses for the psalm are different in this book from the verses recommended by the Church for the selected occasion. This is indicated by the advisory "(Resp. only)" at the end of the index response entry. Recommended verses for the chosen occasion may be found in *Lectionary for Mass*, Vol. IV. When the verses are different from those in this book, they may be recited, or chanted using a simple psalm tone.

Psalm Responses

Common of the Blessed Virgin Mary
Blessed be the name of the Lord for ever. 195
You are the highest honor of our race 214

RCIA

Entrance into the Order of Catechumens
Blessed the people the Lord has chosen
to be his own 222

Presentation of the Creed
Lord, you have the words of everlasting life 41, 60, 220

Presentation of the Lord's Prayer
The Lord is my shepherd;
there is nothing I shall want 43, 71, 94, 139, 208

Christian Initiation Apart from the Easter Vigil
Create a clean heart in me, O God (Resp. only) 47, 63
For ever I will sing the goodness of the Lord
(Resp. only) 18, 20, 128
Let all the earth cry out to God with joy
(Resp. only) 77, 133
My soul is thirsting for you, O Lord my God
(Resp. only) 127, 156, 186
O Lord, our God, how wonderful your name
in all the earth 88
The Lord has done great things for us;
we are filled with joy 13, 48, 181
The Lord is my light and my salvation
(Resp. only) 39, 98, 210
The Lord is my shepherd; there is nothing I shall want
(Resp. only) 43, 71, 94, 139, 192, 208

Conferral of Infant Baptism
Taste and see the goodness of the Lord
(Resp. only) 45, 148, 151, 154, 221
The Lord is my light and my salvation
(Resp. only) 39, 98, 210
The Lord is my shepherd;
there is nothing I shall want 43, 71, 94, 139, 208

Reception of Baptized Christians into the Full Communion of the Catholic Church
My soul is thirsting for you, O Lord my God 127, 156
The Lord is my light and my salvation
(Resp. only) 39, 98, 210

Confirmation
Lord, send out your spirit, and renew the face of the earth
(Resp. only) 53, 84, 85
Proclaim his marvelous deeds to all the nations
(Resp. only) 97
The Lord is my shepherd;
there is nothing I shall want 43, 71, 94, 139, 208

Anointing of the Sick
In every age, O Lord, you have been our refuge
(Resp. only) 161
Like a deer that longs for running streams,
my soul longs for you, my God 61

My soul is thirsting for you, O Lord my God
(Resp. only) 127, 156, 186
O bless the Lord, my soul (Resp. only) 32
Our eyes are fixed on the Lord, pleading for his mercy
(Resp. only) 132
Taste and see the goodness of the Lord
(Resp. only) 45, 148, 151, 154, 221
The Lord is kind and merciful, slow to anger,
and rich in compassion (Resp. only) 162
To you, O Lord, I lift my soul (Resp. only) 10, 209

Conferral of the Sacrament of Marriage
Blessed are those who fear the Lord 189
I will bless the Lord at all times. 221
Taste and see the goodness of the Lord. 148, 221
The earth is full of the goodness of the Lord
(Resp. only) 54
The Lord is kind and merciful
(Resp. only) 42, 110, 112, 114
The Lord's kindness is everlasting to those who fear him
(Resp. only) 92

For the Church
Go out to all the world and tell the Good News 118, 155
O God, let all the nations praise you (Resp. only) 79, 150
Our eyes are fixed on the Lord, pleading for his mercy
(Resp. only) 132
Proclaim his marvelous deeds to all the nations
(Resp. only) 97
Remember your mercies, O Lord (Resp. only) 168
The Lord has revealed to the nations his saving power
(Resp. only) 78, 176
Their message goes out through all the earth
(Resp. only) 201
You are a priest for ever, in the line of Melchizedek. 91

For a Council or Synod or For a Spiritual or Pastoral Meeting
Lord, you have the words of everlasting life 41, 60, 220

For Ministers of the Church
I will bless the Lord at all times (Resp. only) 221
Proclaim his marvelous deeds to all the nations
(Resp. only) 97

For the Laity
Blessed be the name of the Lord for ever
(Resp. only) 195
We are his people: the sheep of his flock
(Resp. only) 73, 122

For the Unity of Christians
Let us go rejoicing to the house of the Lord
(Resp. only) 8, 194
The Lord is my shepherd;
there is nothing I shall want 43, 71, 94, 139, 208
The stone rejected by the builders
has become the cornerstone (Resp. only) 72
We are his people: the sheep of his flock
(Resp. only) 73, 122

Gospel Acclamation Verses

ALPHABETICAL INDEX

Psalm Responses

Gospel Acclamation Verses